SCOTTISH LEGENDARY TALES

By the same author

WELSH LEGENDARY TALES

Before he knew what he was doing his feet were tapping

SCOTTISH LEGENDARY TALES

Told by
Elisabeth Sheppard-Jones

with illustrations by Paul Hogarth

THOMAS NELSON AND SONS LTD · EDINBURGH

THOMAS NELSON AND SONS LTD
Parkside Works Edinburgh 9
36 Park Street London W1
117 Latrobe Street Melbourne C1

THOMAS NELSON AND SONS (AFRICA) (Pty) LTD
P.O. Box 9881 Johannesburg

THOMAS NELSON AND SONS (CANADA) LTD
91–93 Wellington Street West   Toronto 1

THOMAS NELSON AND SONS
18 East 41st Street New York 17, N.Y.

SOCIÉTÉ FRANÇAISE D'ÉDITIONS NELSON
97 rue Monge Paris 5

———

Printed in Great Britain by
Thomas Nelson (Printers) Ltd, London and Edinburgh

Contents ꙮ

Illustrations ❧

Acknowledgment

The verses on p. 174 are reprinted from *Scottish Folk-lore and Folk Life* by Donald A. Mackenzie by kind permission of Messrs Blackie & Son Limited.

The Kingdom of the Green Mountains ⪜

THERE were three soldiers who decided to set off on their separate ways to seek their fortunes. One of them was a sergeant, another a corporal and the third a private.

On the evening of the second day, the sergeant came to a splendid palace, and, as he was tired and hungry, he asked at the gate if he would be allowed to rest and eat there. A beautiful lady came to the gate as he was talking to the guard.

'Of course, you may come in,' she said. 'I shall like to listen to your tales, for it is said that soldiers and sailors are good story-tellers.'

The sergeant followed her inside, and was delighted when the lady told him that his dinner would soon be ready.

'I am sure,' she said, smiling at him, 'that you are hungry and thirsty.'

Darkness fell, and a candle was lit. Soon, servants arrived with the food which was placed on the table before him. There were dishes of every kind of delicious meat and fish.

'We do not have any light at our meals here,' explained the lady, 'so I hope you will take the dish you like best, and be able to eat it in the dark.'

'Certainly,' agreed the sergeant. 'If that is your custom, I will do as you say.'

Then she extinguished the candle, and he set to work on the dish he had chosen. He was about to take the first mouthful, when she struck her foot on the floor. Immediately two officers of the guard hurried in.

'Seize this rascal,' ordered the lady, 'and put him in prison.'

The officers took away the wretched man, and put him in prison, where he was fed on bread and water.

On the following evening, the corporal came to the same palace, and exactly the same thing happened to him. He, too, was finally put in prison with the sergeant, and he, too, was fed only on bread and water.

The evening after that, the private came to the palace. He had been walking for a longer time than the others, and was weak from lack of food. The lady came to him at the gate, and spoke to him.

'I understand,' she said, 'that you are a soldier, and soldiers and sailors are said to be good story-tellers. Come inside.'

She took him in, and sat him down on a comfortable chair.

'Dinner will come to you in a short time,' she told him.

Night came on, and the private began to wonder why the dinner was so long in coming. He was faint with hunger, and was delighted when, at last, the servants arrived with the marvellous array of dishes.

'The custom of this place,' the lady said to him, 'is not to have any light at meals. Will you please take the dish you like best and start your dinner?'

Then she crossed to the candle, and blew it out. At this, the soldier rose, put his two arms around her, and kissed her.

'The food is good,' he said, 'but I prefer yourself to it.'

She struck her foot on the floor, and called for a light. A servant appeared with many candles, and she and the soldier sat down and had dinner together. They spent many hours talking. She asked him if he had any education, and when he said he had,

2

she asked to see his handwriting. Finally, she asked him, ' Will you marry me ? '

' Indeed and I will,' said the soldier. ' But first tell me who you are.'

' I am the daughter of the King of the Green Mountains,' she said, ' but I have no desire to marry a king or a knight. I prefer to marry an ordinary, handsome fellow like yourself. I have a large estate and plenty of gold and silver.'

Then they appointed a day for their marriage.

The next morning, after breakfast, the princess took a gold purse out of her pocket, gave the soldier money to get a suit of clothes for himself, and sent him to a good tailor. The tailor made the suit while he waited, and, when he had finished, the tailor's mother whispered to her son, 'Go a part of the way with the soldier. He will be seized with thirst. Give him this apple, and he will fall asleep.'

The princess, in her coach, was to meet the soldier on his way back to the palace. He and the tailor set off, and on the way they sat down to rest. When the soldier said he was thirsty, the tailor gave him the apple, and after he had eaten it he fell asleep. When the lady arrived, she told the tailor to awake her lover. The tailor shook him from side to side, but the fellow could not be awakened. The lady took a gold ring out of her pocket, and gave it to the tailor.

' Give this to the soldier when he awakes,' she said, ' and tell him I will meet him here tomorrow. He may spend the night with you at your house.'

The next morning, after breakfast, the tailor gave the soldier the gold ring. But, before they set out, the tailor's mother whispered to her son, ' Here is a pear to give the soldier when he is thirsty on the way ; it will make him fall asleep. Perhaps

3

then the daughter of the King of the Green Mountains will fall to your happy lot.'

On the way the soldier complained of thirst, and was given the pear and again fell asleep. The lady arrived in her coach, and she could scarcely believe her eyes when she saw her future husband asleep once again by the roadside. The tailor, on her instructions, tried to waken him, but failed. The lady then took a penknife out of her pocket, and gave it to the tailor.

' Please give this to the young man when he wakes up,' she said, ' and tell him I will meet him here tomorrow.'

When the soldier awoke, he returned to the tailor's home. The tailor gave him the penknife and the princess's message.

After breakfast the next day, the tailor's mother whispered to her son, ' It will be of no use to give him an apple or a pear today, for he will be suspicious. When you arrive at the spot where you sit down to rest, put this pin in the back of his coat, and, if he was sleepy before, he will be seven times sleepier this time.'

The tailor did as he was told, and, as soon as he put the pin in the back of the coat, the soldier fell asleep. The princess arrived as usual, but this time, with her in the coach, she had two strong men.

' Is he asleep again today ? ' she asked the tailor.

' He is, my lady,' replied the tailor.

' Try to waken him,' she said.

The tailor tried, but he could not be wakened, so the lady asked the strong men to lift him into the coach. But the magic of the pin in his coat was very powerful, and he could not be lifted.

The princess sighed. ' Oh well, Tailor,' she said, ' I can do no more. Give the soldier this gold pin when he awakes. I will not come to meet him any more.'

After she had gone, the tailor took out the pin from the soldier's coat, and he awakened. The tailor gave him the lady's gold pin, and told him she would not come again.

'Will you return with me again tonight?' asked the rogue of a tailor.

'No, indeed I will not!' cried the soldier. 'I wish that I had not returned with you so often. This time I will go my own way. Goodbye.'

The soldier went on his way, and he asked everyone he met which was the way to the Kingdom of the Green Mountains. But no-one had heard of it. One day he came to a village where he saw an old man, mending with pieces of turf the roof of a house.

'You are very old to be doing that work,' said the soldier.

'I am old,' replied the old man, 'but my father is older than I.'

'Is your father still alive?' asked the soldier.

'He is,' said the old man. 'And may I ask where you are going?'

'I am going to the Kingdom of the Green Mountains,' the soldier told him.

'Well,' said the old man, 'although I am old and have heard many things in my life, I have never heard of that kingdom. Perhaps my father knows about it.'

'Where is your father?' asked the soldier.

'He is bringing the turf to me,' said the old man, 'and will be here in a short while, when you may ask him about this kingdom of which you speak.'

Soon the old man's father arrived, wheeling a barrow full of turf.

'Good gracious, old man!' exclaimed the soldier. 'How old you are!'

'Indeed, I am old,' agreed the old man, 'but my father is older than I.'

'And is your father still alive?' asked the soldier.

'Yes, he is; he is over there, cutting the turf,' said the old man.

They went to the man who was cutting the turf, and the soldier marvelled to see a man so old, working so hard.

'I am old,' said the turf-cutter, 'yet my father is older than I.'

'And is your father still alive?' asked the soldier.

'Indeed, he is,' said the old man. 'He is hunting birds in the hills.'

'Have you ever heard of the Kingdom of the Green Mountains?' asked the soldier.

'I have not,' he replied, 'but perhaps my father has, and when he comes home tonight, you may ask him.'

In the evening, the fowler came home and the soldier asked him if he had heard of the kingdom for which he was searching. The fowler said he had not, but he added, 'I am going to the hills tomorrow, and when I blow a whistle that I have, there is not a kingdom in the world from which birds will not come to me; so that I shall find out if there be such a kingdom as the one of which you speak.'

After breakfast the next day, the soldier and the fowler went to the hills, and, when the fowler blew his whistle, the birds gathered to him from every corner of the earth. And the last to arrive was a large eagle.

'You wretch!' cried the fowler. 'What has kept you so far behind the others?'

'I had a much greater distance to fly than they,' explained the eagle.

'Where have you come from?' asked the fowler.

(2,531)

' I have come this very day from the Kingdom of the Green Mountains,' said the eagle.

' Well ! ' said the fowler. ' There is a man here whom you must carry on your back to that Kingdom.'

And the soldier climbed on the eagle's back, and they made the long journey to the Kingdom of the Green Mountains. When they arrived, the soldier was tired and starving, and the eagle left him at the house of the gardener to the King of the Green Mountains, where the gardener's wife was very good to him, and fed him and gave him shelter. The soldier learnt from her that the daughter of the King was soon to be married.

' I must see her ! ' he cried out in despair. ' Somehow I must see her ! '

' Take this basket of apples,' said the kind woman, ' and tell her they are from the gardener. Deliver them into no-one's hands but her own.'

The servants tried to take the basket of fruit from him when he reached the palace door, but the soldier insisted on seeing the princess herself. At first she did not recognise him, so, after he had passed her the apples, he handed her the gold ring she had once given him. She took hold of it, looked at it, and saw her own name written inside it.

' Where did you find this ring ? ' she asked.

' Do you remember the soldier whom you sent to a tailor for a suit of clothes ? ' he asked.

' I think that I do,' she replied. ' Have you any further proof ? '

' I have,' he said. And he took out the penknife, and handed it to her.

' Have you still further proof ? ' she asked.

' I have,' he said. And he gave her the gold pin.

' I know now who you are,' she said, and she kissed him.

The man whom she had intended to marry was sent away from the palace, and a day was fixed for her to wed the soldier.

On the wedding day, the soldier begged the daughter of the King of the Green Mountains to have pity on his former companions, the sergeant and the corporal, so she released them from prison. And they all made a feast and rejoicing, and, if they have not ceased eating and drinking, then they are at it still.

The Farmer and the Fairy Hillock ⚓

NOW, perhaps you do not know that in the Hebrides, Orkney and Shetland, and on the mainland north of the Caledonian Canal, there were once several hundred green hillocks. They looked ordinary grassy mounds, but, in fact, they were the dwellings of the Highland fairies. These fairies were usually kind and helpful to the Highland folk, but the destruction of one of their mounds was sure to make them very angry—as a farmer called Donal once discovered to his cost.

Donal had decided to plough a field on his farm. It had never been ploughed before, and in the middle of it stood a ' broch ' or hillock.

' That must be levelled,' Donal told his labourers, pointing his finger towards the offending hillock.

The men muttered amongst themselves, and eventually one one man spoke out.

' Is that wise, do you think, sir ? ' he asked.

' Wise ? ' queried Donal. ' Of course it's wise, man ! You can't plough a field and leave a great mound in the middle of it. What's this nonsense you are talking ? '

' It is said that the fairies live there,' came the answer, ' and he who disturbs them will live to regret it.'

There was more murmuring from the men, accompanied by nods and cries of, ' Aye, that is true ! '

' This is silly talk ! ' cried Donal. ' Are you children, to believe such tales ? Now, get on with the work, and no more arguing lest you find yourselves without jobs. I'll lend a hand myself to prove to. you that there is nothing in these foolish imaginings.'

After some more grumbling, the men finally agreed to do the work. Under the grass the hillock was made of many stones, and it proved to be a longer job than it had appeared at first. Two days went by, and still Donal and his men had not managed to remove completely the hillock. On the evening of the second day, the labourer who had spoken earlier on behalf of the men came to Donal with bad news.

' I have been milking the cows,' he said, ' and there is something wrong with them. The brindled one called Jeannie is mortal sick, and the rest of the herd look sick, too. It is the curse of the fairies. I told you that the hillock should never have been disturbed.'

Donal was too worried to reply. He hurried to the cow-shed to look at his precious herd. Jeannie was already dead, and, it was as the hired man had said, the others appeared sick. The shed was loud with the bellowing of the few which still had the strength to make some noise.

Back in the farm house, the anxious Donal confided in his wife.

' You should not have touched the hillock,' his wife told him gently.

' You believe that old wives' tale, too ? ' said her husband.

' Yes,' she said, ' I do. The cattle have the plague : there is your proof.'

Donal shook his head, and refused to be convinced. The work on the broch went on.

The next day, Donal's wife was alone in the farmhouse when

' I will stay where I am,' replied the fairy crossly

there came a tap at the kitchen door. On opening the door, she
saw there a tiny creature, no more than two feet high.

' Why, if it isn't a fairy woman ! ' exclaimed the farmer's
wife. ' Come in, come in, please.'

' I will stay where I am,' replied the fairy crossly. ' Tell your
husband that I have lived in the broch in his field for more time
than I care to remember, and that he will have further cause to
repent for disturbing me and mine.'

' Then it was you who cursed the cattle,' said the farmer's
wife. But there was no reply : the little woman had disappeared.

When Donal heard the story of this visit, he laughed. And
work in his field went on. But that evening, when he was
walking home alone along a grassy track leading to his house, the
fairy woman suddenly appeared in front of him, and, shaking
her fist at him, she screamed out, ' How dare you go on with
your wicked work after you have been warned ! More of your
cows will be dead this very night as reward for your evil labour.'

The fairy disappeared as quickly as she had come, leaving
Donal at last convinced that he had indeed been disturbing a fairy
dwelling-place. He ran to the cow-shed and found that three

more of his cows had died that day, and news soon reached him that the cattle plague was spreading to the neighbouring farms. He gave instructions for work on the broch to cease, and the stones that had been removed were carefully put back in place. In spite of this, the plague still raged. Poor Donal was beside himself with worry, and now he had to face the anger of his neighbours, who told him in no few words that they were suffering unfairly for his stupidity.

It was Donal's wife who suggested the cure for the evil which had befallen them.

'The good favour of the little people may be won again only by lighting the *Teine eigin*,' she said.

Teine eigin was the fire of need ; and this was the way of it. Messengers were sent round the district to say that all fires must be extinguished, and the hearths allowed to grow cold. This being done, the whole population—mainly farmers and farm workers and their families—gathered together on a small island in the middle of the nearest river.

'This island is too small,' grumbled Donal. 'There is scarcely room even for the old women to sit down.'

As he spoke, a fat miller fell into the water, and had to be hauled back on to dry land, where his wife held on to him tightly so that he shouldn't fall in again.

'We must be surrounded by water,' said Donal's wife.

Then, by rubbing together two dry sticks—in the way that Boy Scouts today are taught to start a fire—she managed to get a light. Into this flame, the people stuck long torches of wood, which, carrying high before them, they took home to relight their household fires.

'I hope that all this nonsense is going to be of some avail,' said Donal.

THE FARMER AND THE FAIRY HILLOCK

His wife was a woman of wisdom ; she just smiled at him, and said nothing. But she was not a bit surprised when, next morning, the sick cattle showed signs of recovery. The plague had left the district.

Donal never again touched the green hillock, and, so far as we know, he was never heard to say again that he didn't believe in fairies.

The Shepherd and the Fairy Hillock ⤳●

AND here is another tale about a fairy hillock. There was once a shepherd who, unlike Donal, knew that the green hillocks he saw during his long wanderings with his sheep were the homes of the fairies. One night, as he was making his way to his stone cottage for his supper, he thought he heard the sound of hammering. He stopped and listened. It was a dark, velvety night, and nothing much to be seen but the shadowy shapes of the fields and hills. Somewhere an owl hooted, and then there was silence.

'Must have been my imagination,' the shepherd told himself. 'Not very likely that the blacksmith is at work in an empty field, and at night-time, too.'

He laughed softly at his own joke, and was about to move on, when he heard it again. *Tap tap tap, tappitty tap, tappitty tap.* The shepherd moved a little to his left : the sounds became fainter. He moved to the right : the sounds became louder. He moved further to the right ; and there, in front of him, he could just see the familiar outline of a fairy hillock. He put his ear to the side of the hillock and—*tap tap tap, tappitty tap, tappitty tap*—there was no mistaking it, the hammering was going on inside.

'Aha, the fairies are at work,' thought the shepherd. 'I'd dearly like to see what they are doing.'

Very quietly he scraped away some earth and stone, and, putting an eye to the hole he had made, he found he could see right into the fairy dwelling place. It was full of tiny men and women. Some of the men were working with hammers and chisels, and they appeared to be making a figure of stone.

One little man, an onlooker, was jumping up and down with excitement.

' Make it bonnie,' he was crying out to the workers. ' Make it as bonnie as Meg is herself.

The shepherd gasped : Meg was the name of his wife, and, as he watched the shaping of the stone, he recognised that it was being made in her image. There was her sweet oval face, her little turned-up nose, her huge eyes ; there was her thick shower of hair ; there was her trim figure, and slim neat feet. Why were the little folk doing this ? He searched his mind for an answer, and then he remembered that the fairies like to kidnap humans who attract them, and that one way of doing this was to magic them away by leaving in their place an effigy of some sort.

He ran home as fast as his legs could carry him, desperately hoping that the fairies, who had swift and secret ways of travelling, would not have finished their work and arrived before him. To his great relief, his pretty wife greeted him at the door. He embraced her so affectionately that she smilingly said, ' Why, my dear, anyone would think you had not seen me for a year.' He patted her shoulder affectionately, and made no reply.

While they were having their supper together, there was a noise of rustling and whispering outside. The shepherd guessed the reason for this but, not wishing to worry his wife, he made no comment.

' Did you hear something ? ' asked Meg.

' It is but the whistling of the wind,' said the shepherd.

' No, no,' insisted Meg. ' There is something wrong in the byre. Won't you go out and see if the cattle are all right ? '

Although the shepherd's main charges were sheep, he did

keep a few cattle to provide himself and his family with butter, milk and cheese.

'It is but the whistling of the wind,' repeated the shepherd. He was determined not to leave his wife, nor the safety of his house, while the mischievous fairies were about at night, and at last he managed to persuade Meg that the noises she heard were perfectly natural ones.

With the coming of daylight, the shepherd knew it was safe to venture outside. He went quickly to the byre, and found the cattle unharmed. But, in the far corner of the shed, under some rough sacking, lay something that looked like a body. It was the stone effigy of Meg. He covered it over with straw, and returned to the house, where he managed to persuade Meg that she should visit a sick neighbour that afternoon. As soon as she had left, the shepherd went back to the byre, and dragged out the statue. He pulled it over the cobbled stones of the yard, through the back door and into the kitchen. With a mighty heave, he hurled it on to a huge fire that was burning in the hearth. And, although the figure appeared to be made from stone, it instantly vanished up the chimney in a flame of such gold and rose and turquoise that the shepherd had to shield his eyes against the wonder of it.

Fairy Workmen ❦

IN the main, Scottish fairies are pleasant, friendly creatures, anxious to be good and helpful to the humans they meet. Certainly, they were once very helpful to a poor fisherman called Colin who lived on the Island of Lewis. During the long winter, Colin had managed to catch very few fish, but he was sure that matters would improve for him if only he could fish in deeper waters. To do this he would need a mast on his boat, and, alas, he had no mast. Neither had he the money to buy one. On the island there were few trees of value to a timber merchant, and as all the timber had to be imported, wood was very expensive. Colin knew he could never save enough money to buy wood for his mast, and the only bit of wood he had in the world was the handle of an old hammer.

'And a pretty poor mast I should make out of this,' he said ruefully, as he turned over the handle in his hand. Then an idea came to him. 'But the fairies! The fairies could make a mast out of it!' he cried.

Late that night he hastened to a nearby hillock where he knew the fairies lived. He threw down the hammer outside, at the same time calling out in a loud voice, 'Men of Peace! Turn this hammer into a fine mast for me before dawn breaks.'

Colin was confident that they could do this, but he was also curious to know how they would do it. So he hid close by.

17

They began to examine the hammer

Several of the little men came out of the hillock. They began to examine the hammer.

' What a difficult task the man who has come from the living men has given us this night ! ' exclaimed one of them. He set to work on the wooden handle with furious energy, cutting at it with a tiny knife, muttering magic fairy words over it, binding slivers of the wood with gold and silver threads—all to no avail. And when he realised he had failed, he gave a groan and fell down dead.

Another of the fairy men then stepped forward, picked up the hammer, and set about trying to complete the work at which his brother had perished. As he worked, he cried out, ' My bellows, my hammers, and my anvil ; my poverty, my distress and my foolishness ; to make a mast of a hand mallet ; my weightiest violence and my destruction be on the hand that

18

sent in the hammer, for it cost my brother his heart's blood. Nevertheless, I will do it ! I will do it ! '

On and on the little man worked, sometimes muttering to himself, sometimes singing. In the early hours of the morning, Colin fell asleep, and when he awoke there was no sign of the fairies. But there, where he had thrown down the hammer handle, lay a fine, strong mast, which Colin carried home in triumph. From that day on, he was able to cast his nets wider and wider, and his little boat sailed bravely into the strongest winds and over the stormiest seas, and never came to harm.

Now, when Colin had overheard the wild words of the fairy workman he had been tempted to utter a blessing over him, for no matter on what work the fairies are engaged, it is always easy to stop them at any time by saying a blessing. He had kept quiet only because he so desperately needed that mast for his boat.

On one occasion, blessing the fairies proved most unfortunate. Across the Dornoch Firth there stretches a bank of shingle and sand, known as the Noisy Bridge because of the rushing noise made by the swirling waters as they meet over it. This bank was not always there but, it is said, the fairies became tired of crossing from Sutherland to Ross-shire in their cockle-shell boats, so they decided to build a bridge across the firth. This bridge was to be a more wonderful feat of engineering than any built by human hands ; the pillars were to be of gold, the girders of silver, the great arches to be studded with precious stones, the roadway itself to be of marble and alabaster. Unfortunately, when the work was half completed, a man passing that way stopped to gaze at its magnificence. He had never seen anything like it in his life. And, not knowing that it was the craftsmanship of the fairies, he lifted up his hands and cried out aloud to the skies, ' God bless these workmen ! '

At this, there was a great outcry from the little folk, who began to groan and cry and shout. And the hundreds of fairy workmen who were building the bridge leapt from the pillars and the girders and the arches into the sea beneath. They never returned to their work, which has long since gone to ruin, but the remains of which, no doubt, could be found far underneath the shingle, should anyone care to look for them.

The Tale of the Hump-Backed Men ॐ

THERE were once two hump-backed men who were friends. They were called Robert and Thomas. One Saturday night, Thomas visited Robert in his little house. They ate and drank together, and discussed the latest village gossip. They laughed and joked and told each other some of the old, old stories in the light of the peat-fire flame. Then, as it was nearing midnight, Thomas said he must go home and, bidding his friend goodnight, he set out across the fields which separated their two cottages. In one of these fields, near a green knoll, there was a fairy ring. Thomas knew it well, and had always suspected that occasionally the fairies danced and sang in it. He was not very surprised, therefore, when this night he heard music coming from the spot as he approached it. He stopped to listen, and at that moment the moon came out from behind the clouds and lit up the tiny figures who were dancing in the ring. And—oh !—with what grace they danced, and in what sweet voices they sang ! Thomas was entranced, and sat down near by to watch and listen. The fairies were dancing to the music of a rhyme on the days of the week.

' On Sunday we rest and play,' they sang,
' On Monday we wash all day,
  On Tuesday we plough and sow,
  On Thursday we . . . '

He found he could dance as gracefully as the lightest fairy

Thomas had a quick ear, and instantly noticed that they had forgotten to mention Wednesday. Almost without thinking, he called out :

'On Wednesday we knead our dough.'

The fairies at once caught it up and, dancing with renewed vigour, they sang :

'On Sunday we rest and play,
On Monday we wash all day,
On Tuesday we plough and sow,
On Wednesday we knead our dough,
On Thursday we boil our broth,
On Friday we weave our cloth,
On Saturday we dance—and dance—and dance !'

As they sang out the last words, they rushed out of the ring, caught hold of Thomas, and dragged him back with them. He sang and danced with them for the rest of the night, and, in spite of his hump-back, he found he could dance as gracefully as the lightest fairy. The green grass beneath his feet felt as soft and springy as a cloud of swansdown, and his usually rough and rasping voice was now as clear and sweet as the voices of his fairy companions.

When daylight came, the fairies took Thomas with them into the green knoll which was their home. He went unresisting, and for a year and a day he stayed with them, sharing their work and their play. When it was time for him to return to the outside world, a spokesman of the fairies said to him, ' Thomas, you have been a good companion and have greatly aided us with your music and your dancing. We are grateful to you. What reward in friendship may we give you ? '

There was one thing Thomas had wanted all his life : he wanted to be like other men. He wanted to walk tall and upright, with a back that was strong and straight and smooth.

' Take away my hump,' he begged them.

The words were scarcely out of his mouth before his wish was granted.

He raced across the fields to tell the good news to his dear friend Robert. Robert was digging in his garden.

' Look, Robert, look ! ' shouted Thomas in his great excitement. ' The fairies have taken away my hump.'

' Where have you been during this last year ? ' demanded Robert, somewhat crossly.

' With the fairies,' replied Thomas. ' And look, look what they have done for me ! ' He swung round that Robert might see his straight back. Then he told his friend about the fairy rhyme, and about how he had corrected the singing of it, and of how the fairies had rewarded him in friendship.

' Is this not a wonderful tale, my friend ? ' he asked, when he had finished.

But Robert had a black nature, and was secretly jealous of his friend's good fortune. He said nothing.

' Are you not glad to see me back ? ' asked the disappointed Thomas. ' For, indeed, I am glad to see you.'

He held out his hand, but Robert did not take it ; he just went on with his digging, planning in his mind how he, too, might benefit from fairy gratitude.

The next Saturday night, Robert went to the field where Thomas had told him the fairy ring might be found. There he watched and waited until, at last, his patience was rewarded and he heard the fairies singing, and saw them dancing in the ring.

> ' On Sunday we rest and play,' they sang,
> ' On Monday we wash all day,
> On Tuesday we plough and sow,
> On Wednesday we knead our dough, . . . '

Robert had no ear for music and rhythm, neither was he as quick in the uptake as his friend Thomas. Not noticing that the fairies were singing the rhyme correctly and had not left out any of the days of the week, he started to call out, ' On Thursday . . .', when they had already finished the Thursday line. This had the effect of putting them all wrong, and they had to start again.

> ' On Sunday we rest and play,' they began,
> ' On Monday we wash all day,
> On Tuesday we plough and sow,
> On Wednesday we knead our dough,
> On Thursday we boil our broth,
> On Friday we weave our cloth,
> On Saturday we hit—and kick—and pinch ! '

As they sang out these last words, they laid hold of Robert and, pulling him into the fairy ring, they put their words into effect, until at last they left him alone, bruised and breathless upon the ground. When he had the strength to get up, the sun had appeared over the edge of the hills and there was no sign of the fairies. Robert put his hand to his back in the rather forlorn hope that the fairies had been kinder to him than they had appeared to be. Alas ! not only was his own hump still there, but the fairies had added the one they had removed from Thomas's back. This, then, was the reward Robert received for harbouring envy in his heart.

The Piper of Sutherland 〰

ONCE upon a time there was a famous piper in Sutherland—let us call him Iain—who played the bagpipes more skilfully than any piper had ever done before him. When he played the rousing marches of Scotland, the young men who heard him were filled with determination to be brave in battle and to perform great deeds of daring, whilst the old men dreamt of past splendour and the fame that had been gained on the Scottish battlefields. If he played soft melodies of heart-rending beauty, the young girls would sigh for they knew not what, and the old women would mourn for their lost youth. But when he played the gay and lilting reels of his country, then the feet of the young men and the young girls were set a-dancing and a-twirling, and the hands of the old men and the old women were set a-clapping and a-tapping. And there would be laughter and happiness, and the cares and worries of the world would be forgotten.

It is not surprising, then, that Iain was always in demand at weddings or at any occasion when there was something to celebrate, and the people wished to dance and make merry. Neither is it surprising that the fairies should soon come to hear of his musical skill.

Now, it is well known that certain fairies, however enchanting their own music may be, dearly love to hear the music that is played by mortal men, especially if that music is played upon the bagpipes. And the Sutherland fairies planned to capture Iain that he might play to them in their fairy halls underground.

One day, Iain was invited to play at the wedding of a neighbour's daughter. It was a big wedding, and nearly everyone in the district had been invited. When the ceremony was over and the feasting and the drinking had begun, Iain was asked to play. And such was his skill that day, even the old folk got to their feet, and joined in the dancing. On and on played Iain, and, whenever he stopped to rest, there were shouts and cries for, ' More music, Iain, more music ! '—and he began again. He played far into the night until, at last, even the liveliest of the dancers was too tired to ask for more, and Iain was able to set out on his long walk home. If the dancers were worn out, even more so was Iain. When he was half-way home, he lay down on a grassy bank, and, with his bagpipes by his side, he fell asleep. It was there that the fairies found him and, with pokes and pinches, aroused him from his sleep. Had Iain not been too tired to recognise the danger, he would have jumped to his feet and raced to the safety of his home. As it was, he was flattered that the fairies should bother with him, and he answered their questions cheerfully.

' Are you Iain the Piper ? ' asked one little man.

' Aye, that I am,' replied Iain.

' Will you rest with us for an hour or so ? ' asked a little lady, whose green dress was the colour of wet moss.

' Aye, thank you kindly, that I will do,' replied Iain.

' And will you come to our fairy halls underground ? ' asked another little man.

Iain hesitated for a moment, and then agreed to go with them. It was not often that a human had such a chance offered to him, and it would be a fine story to tell his wife when he saw her in the morning. He let the fairies lead him to a nearby hillock, at the side of which was a cave entrance. The fairies poured through this, followed by Iain carrying his precious bagpipes. They trailed down a long, dark passage until they reached a huge hall which was lit by a thousand fairy candles, casting a thousand shadows among the chattering and laughing fairies, some of whom were eating off plates of gold and drinking from goblets of silver, while the rest danced and sang to the music of their own fairy pipers.

As soon as Iain stepped into this hall, his weariness left him. He felt gay and carefree, and when he was asked if he would play his bagpipes for the fairy company, he readily agreed. He played as one bewitched. The fairies were delighted with him, and, if they had never heard music like his before, he had never seen dancing like theirs before. The faster he played, the faster they danced. Their feet seemed scarcely to touch the ground, and their flimsy, green garments floating through the cavernous hall looked to the charmed Iain like seaweed waving and curling at the bottom of the ocean.

He played for what he thought was an hour or two, but, in fairyland, time has no meaning. Above ground, his wife waited anxiously for him to come home, and when he had not appeared by the next day, she went to the neighbour whose daughter had been married on the day of his disappearance.

' Where is Iain, my husband ? ' she asked.

' He left when the wedding party broke up early this morning,' the neighbour assured her.

A search party was organised, and Iain's friends and family looked for him high and low. He was nowhere to be found. The months went by, and still there was no sign of him. The years went by, and still there was no news of him. People began to forget him. His wife married again. And that might have been the end of it, had it not been for an old nurse called Meg.

THE PIPER OF SUTHERLAND

Meg was a friend of the fairies, and very occasionally, when there was sickness among them which they were unable to cure with fairy herbs, they sent for her. One day, years after Iain's disappearance, a fairy messenger visited Meg and begged her to come below ground where a fairy baby lay sick and ailing. Meg put on her bonnet, and set out. She reached the hillock, entered the cave and walked along the long, dark passage. And there in the fairy hall she saw Iain playing his bagpipes. Before she had a chance to speak to him, she was led to another room where she tended the baby. She wondered if it was really Iain she had seen, and, on her way back through the hall, she spoke to the piper.

'Is it Iain the Piper then?' she asked.

'Aye,' he replied, 'but what's that to you?'

'I remember you,' said Meg. 'When I was a young girl, I remember going to a wedding where you played. I have never forgotten your music.'

Iain gazed at the old woman before him. She was bent with rheumatism, her face was wrinkled, her hair was white. He shook his head.

'When you were a *young* girl? I don't understand.'

'You have been here a long time, Iain the Piper. I recall that you disappeared soon after the wedding I speak of.' And she named the girl whose wedding it was.

'But that was last night!' cried Iain. 'Last night the fairies asked me to rest here for an hour after that wedding. Away with you, woman; you are mad, and know not what you say.'

'Remember Angus, the shepherd?' asked Meg. 'He was young when you were young. Last winter they buried him, and his grandchildren came to the funeral. Remember the woodcutter's little boy whom you used to take fishing? His youngest son was married in the kirk last spring. Remember Farmer

The wise man spent some time over his large books of magic

Macleod's babe? You played at her christening, didn't you?
Well, you weren't there to play at her firstborn's christening
yester week.'

Iain shook his head in confusion, refusing to believe what the
old woman told him. He picked up his pipes, and began to play
with great fury, as if by doing so he could forget the unpleasant
news he had just heard.

Meg hurried home, and soon the great news she had brought
with her was round the district. 'Iain the Piper is in fairyland!'
The question was, how to get him out of there. Near by there
lived a wise man who, it was said, had even greater power than
the fairies. As Meg was the only person to have set eyes on Iain
in his fairy surroundings, she was appointed spokesman by the
villagers.

'How may we get the piper out of fairyland?' she asked the
wise man.

At first, there was no reply. The wise man spent some time

30

over his large books of magic, and when, at last, he had found what he wanted, he said, 'Take me to the hillock where lies the entrance to the fairy hall you tell me about.'

Meg led him there, followed at a distance by the curious villagers. The wise man stayed there all night, sometimes muttering words of magic, sometimes consulting his books, sometimes nodding and mumbling to himself.

At dawn, the first cock crowed. The wise man lifted up his hand, and the chattering voices of those who had stayed to watch all night were quiet. There came a faint sound of music from the cave entrance which gradually swelled and swelled until out of the cave marched the piper with his skirling pipes. There was a great gasp from the crowd, and then some of the old men who had known Iain in the years gone by, went up to greet him. But Iain appeared lost and dazed. He didn't recognise his friends. He didn't appear to want to know them. One of them took him home, gave him food and drink, and put him to bed. Iain spoke to no-one, but lay quietly in bed, his pipes by his side, his face turned to the wall. And thus he stayed for many weeks, until, one evening, when he had been left alone for an hour or two, he quietly arose from his bed, took up his pipes, and marched away in the direction of the hillock.

No-one saw him again, and no-one thought it right to try to rescue him again. His only happiness now was with the fairies. Occasionally, on a clear, calm night, his old friends would hear the sound of his beautiful music somewhere in the distance, far, far away. And if you could find that particular green hillock that lies somewhere in Sutherland, it is possible that you, too, might hear, for one enchanted moment, the music of Iain the Piper as he plays for the fairy dancers. For, as far as I know, he is still at it.

The Fiddlers of Strathspey ⍦

A LASTAIR and John were two poor fiddlers who lived in Strathspey. They had so little in the way of worldly goods that they decided to seek their fortune in Inverness. They set out on foot, playing in the villages they passed on the way, sometimes managing to earn a few pence, sometimes earning only a meal or a night's lodging.

' I hope things are going to get better for us in Inverness,' said Alastair, when they were nearly at the end of their journey.

' At any rate, they couldn't get much worse,' replied John. He looked down ruefully at his ragged clothes, and wiggled his toe about in the hole in his shoe.

But, in fact, matters did get worse. When they reached the town, winter had set in, and the snow was thick upon the ground. The fiddlers put their fiddles under their chins, and began to play their gayest jigs, but there was not a soul in the streets to hear them. The good people of Inverness were indoors, crouched over their fires, or cuddled up in their beds.

' We are wasting our time,' sighed John. ' Let us put away our fiddles and find somewhere to shelter from this bitter wind.'

As he spoke, an old man stepped out from the shadows of the deserted street.

' Good evening to you, gentlemen,' he quavered. ' Are you fiddlers, then ? '

' Aye, we are,' answered Alastair, ' but fiddlers without an audience this night, it would seem.'

32

'And fiddlers with empty purses and empty stomachs,' added John.

'I'll fill your purses and your stomachs if you will play for me,' said the old man.

The words were scarcely out of his mouth before John and Alastair had raised their bows to their fiddles. This was better luck than they had dared hope for.

'No, no, not here,' said the old man, putting a restraining hand on Alastair's arm. 'You must follow me, if you will.'

'A strange old man,' whispered John to his friend.

'Let us do as he says,' whispered back Alastair, 'if it will mean money in our purses and food in our stomachs.'

The old man led the way, and, with their heads bowed in the face of the blinding snow, the two fiddlers followed. They went to a place called Tomnahurich Hill, and, when they were half-way up the hill, the old man stopped outside a large house. The house looked deserted; there were no lights in the windows and no sign of any inhabitants. The old man went up to the huge door and, although he didn't knock on it, it opened silently in front of him. The fiddlers stopped, and looked at each other in astonishment. John was a little frightened, and would have run away, had not Alastair urged him to think of the warmth and comfort that possibly awaited them.

Annoyed at the delay, the old man turned and angrily urged them to follow him into the house at once if they intended keeping their part of the bargain. As soon as they had stepped over the threshold, the door shut silently behind them. For the first time, the fiddlers were aware of noise and light and laughter. The old man ushered them through another door and into a magnificent ballroom, the like of which they had never seen before. Beautifully embroidered tapestries hung on the walls;

33

thick carpets of Oriental design lay on the floor, except at the far end where a space had been cleared for dancing ; and the elegant furniture was of rare, carved woods, the seats and backs of the chairs covered with rich brocades and velvets. There was a long table piled high with strange foods such as the root of the silver weed that the farmers plough up in the spring-time, and which was once known as the Seventh Bread ; and the stalks and tops of heather, and young fresh heather-shoots. And there were jugs of goats' milk and of the milk of the red deer hind, and decanters of wine that glowed purple in the candlelight, and baskets of fruit and bowls of yellow cream. The very sight made John and Alastair lick their lips in anticipation. And the hall was full of lovely ladies and handsome gentlemen, dressed in silks and satins and laces and furbelows.

' Help yourselves to some food,' invited the old man, leading them towards the long table.

The fiddlers needed no encouragement. For many minutes neither of them spoke, as they made up for the days when they had been unable to get sufficient food to stay their hunger. When, at last, they could eat and drink no more, John noticed that the old man had disappeared. He pointed out this fact to his companion, who said, ' I certainly didn't see him go, but nothing surprises me in this strange place. Come on, John, get out your fiddle and let's play for that excellent supper we have just eaten.'

The fiddlers began to play, and the nimble and colourful company began to dance. On and on the fiddlers played ; on and on the dancers danced. No-one tired, and it seemed to John and Alastair that only a half-hour or so had passed when the old man reappeared as suddenly as he had disappeared.

' Stop your fiddling now,' he ordered. ' Dawn is nearly here. You must be on your way.'

And with these words, he gave each of them a bag of gold.

'We have scarcely worked hard enough or long enough for this,' said the honest John.

'Take it, and go,' said the old man curtly.

The young men did as they were told, and went on their way, rejoicing at their good fortune.

As they walked towards the town, it was Alastair who first noticed something rather odd.

'These houses are new,' he said. 'I'll swear there were great fields at this spot last night.'

'It was dark last night,' replied John ; 'perhaps you were mistaken. The houses don't look very new to me, and, anyway, houses can't be built in a night.'

'Do you remember that bridge over there, then ?' asked Alastair.

'I can't say that I do,' said John.

'If it had been there, we should have walked across it.'

John was puzzled. The whole town looked different. He decided to ask a passer-by if they were indeed where they thought they were. The first man they met was dressed in clothes the like of which they had never seen before, and when John asked him about the bridge and the houses, he laughed and assured them that bridge and houses had been there for a very long time. He laughed again when he left them, saying, ' You're an odd couple. Are you off to a fancy dress ball, dressed in those funny old clothes ?'

Certainly their clothes were shabby but, otherwise, there was nothing very funny about them, and John and Alastair thought it very rude of the stranger to comment on them, especially since his own clothes were so curious. But when they reached the town, they discovered that the men, women and children were all dressed in this unfamiliar style. The shops were different ; even the accents of the people had changed. Whenever the fiddlers asked questions, they were laughed at ; and wherever they went, they were stared at.

'Let us return to Strathspey,' suggested Alastair.

'There is nothing to keep us here now,' John agreed, 'and I do not like the people. They treat us as if we were complete fools.'

They made their way back to Strathspey. This time they travelled on horseback, with plenty of money for food and lodging. And they played their fiddles for their own pleasure, and for no other reason.

When they reached their home town, they could scarcely believe they were there. This, too, had changed : streets, houses, bridges, people—everything was different. They went to buy bread : the baker was a stranger. They went to the farm for milk : the farmer appeared to have a new wife ; they didn't recognise her nor she them. The children playing in the school-yard didn't greet them as they were used to do ; the school itself had altered—it looked bigger, and the roof was a different colour. They hastened to call on their best friend, James the blacksmith, to tell him of their good fortune and to ask him why everything in Strathspey had altered, and what had happened to their other friends. The blacksmith proved to be a man they had never seen before, and he had never even heard of their friends.

Thoroughly alarmed, the young men made their way to the church where they hoped they might find an answer to the mystery, and where they would certainly find refuge. The little country church they had known all their lives looked bigger and newer than they remembered it, but the churchyard was the same, and they wandered through it, looking at the tombstones. Alastair suddenly clutched John's arm.

'No wonder James the blacksmith was not at home!' he exclaimed. 'Here is his grave.'

John peered at the inscription on the headstone. 'But how is this possible?' he asked. 'When we left Strathspey a few weeks ago James was a young man in his twenties, like ourselves, and here it says he was ninety-three when he died.'

The fiddlers looked at the other graves. All the friends they had known were buried here.

'Alas!' groaned Alastair. 'We played our jigs to the fairies that night in Inverness. Too long we played, too long!'

'It was for but an hour or two,' said John, 'that's all.'

'That is how it seemed to us, but we have been gone over a hundred years,' said Alastair.

The two friends walked sadly into the church, where a service was taking place. Some of the congregation turned their heads to gaze in wonder at the old-fashioned couple as they walked up the aisle.

'In the name of the Father, the Son and the Holy Ghost,' intoned the clergyman in his pulpit.

And at these words, John and Alastair fell to the ground and crumbled into dust.

John Macdonald and the Kelpie ⤳

MANY tales are told about that dreaded beast, the Kelpie, which used to inhabit the lovely lakes of Scotland, luring into the depths of the water its unsuspecting human victims. The Kelpie could assume the shape of man, woman or any animal, but its favourite guise was that of the horse. Beautifully groomed, its chestnut coat glistening and shiny, its long tail flowing in the breeze, its eyes soft and friendly, it would canter up to some fair young girl who, as she stroked the velvet nose, soon found she could not take away her hand. Then the Kelpie would lead her forcibly into the nearest lake, and she would never be seen again.

There was one Kelpie which was particularly troublesome. One day he appeared to some children who were playing beside a lake. He wore a smart bridle and saddle, and one of the children thought it would be fun to catch him, and have a ride on his back. None of the children, of course, suspected that this gentle-looking animal was an evil beast of the lake. The lad mounted the horse easily, and then called out for another boy to get up behind him.

'Room for one more,' cried out this boy, as he seated himself comfortably behind his friend.

A third lad mounted, and he, too, called out, 'Come on, room for one more.'

A fourth lad clambered up behind. 'Room for one more,' and he laughed.

The old man angrily urged them to follow

And so it went on, until there were sixteen boys on the horse's back.

The last boy did not like riding on horseback, and refused to join his friends.

'I don't care if there is room for one more,' he said. 'I'm staying down here. But, I tell you what, I'll lead the horse for you.'

And he put his finger on the horse's head. It was as if a magnet held his finger there, and when he tried to move it, he could not do so. A tremor of fear went through him as he remembered the tales his father sometimes told of the Kelpie. He looked into the eyes of the horse and saw, reflected there, the black evil of the Kelpie's heart. There was one thing he could do to save himself from certain destruction, and this he did. He whipped out a knife from his pocket with his free hand and, gritting his teeth, cut off his finger, and escaped. There was nothing he could do for his playmates, and sorrowfully he watched the wicked Kelpie trot off towards the lake, and disappear under the water with the sixteen helpless boys still sitting on its back.

Now, the boy who escaped knew a very brave man called John Macdonald, who lived near the lake of this Kelpie. When the boy told him of the terrible thing that had happened to his friends, John determined to put an end to the trouble and damage that the water horse had been causing for so long in the neighbourhood. John knew—what the children did not—that the Kelpie received its magic powers from its master, the Devil, and that these powers worked through the magic bridle which it wore.

Every day he went down to the roadside where the Kelpie often lurked, hoping to tempt some riderless traveller on to its back. Many a day he waited, and nothing happened. Then, at last, one evening, he saw a beautiful horse, harmlessly cropping the lush green grass that grew on the verge of the road. No animal could have looked more innocent. John Macdonald might have taken little notice of it, had it not been decked out in a saddle and bridle. This struck him as strange, since the animal appeared to have no rider with it. He went up to it, talking softly and coaxingly. The Kelpie—for such it was—looked up, thinking no doubt that here was the victim it was waiting for. But, instead of mounting the steed, John picked up a thick oak stick and, with a mighty blow, hit the horse such a whack on the nose that the bridle was broken, and the bit fell to the ground. While the beast was still reeling from the blow, Macdonald picked up the bit, put it in his pocket and, brave man that he was, prepared to continue the fight. But the Kelpie was not prepared to fight.

'Hold fast, man,' it said, in a pleading voice. 'Don't hit me again. I am but a poor defenceless animal.'

'You, defenceless? Huh!' John scornfully replied, raising his stick higher.

The Kelpie was enraged by this. 'You'll suffer for what you're doing to me,' it said. 'I have it in my power to wreak terrible vengeance on you.' Then, in a more persuasive voice, it added, 'But I'll do you no harm, no harm at all, if only you will return the bit to me.'

John adamantly refused to do this. 'You're nothing but a wicked Kelpie!' he shouted.

'Yes, that's true,' replied the Kelpie. 'I admit it; but we Kelpies must do what we are told by our master, you know, and sometimes it's very unpleasant for us. Now, please, be a good fellow, and return my bit to me.'

This was a cunning animal with which John Macdonald had to deal, but John himself could be cunning, too.

'Well, I must say, I'm sorry for you,' he lied. 'However, I

It went off, its head lowered and its tail drooping

am curious about something. Tell me why you are so anxious to have back the bit, and then you shall have it back.'

If a horse could smile, the Kelpie would have done so. Gleefully it replied, 'My royal master, the Devil, gives us a magic bridle through which we are able to assume any shape we wish, but when I lose the bit, my magic powers are at an end. Now, please, please, hand back the bit.'

'Is there anything more you have to tell me about it?' asked John.

'If you look through one of the holes of the bit, you will see any number of witches and fairies willing to do your bidding.'

'In that case,' said John, 'I might as well keep the bit, and use it myself. I should like to have witches and fairies as my servants.'

When it heard this, the Kelpie began to rage and storm and stamp its feet upon the ground. John flourished the heavy stick, and soon the beast quietened. John turned round, the bit still in

41

his pocket, and made for home. The Kelpie quietly followed him at a safe distance until John's cottage was in sight, then it quickened its pace, overtook John, and placed itself between the man and the front door of the house.

' I'll not move from here,' screeched the Kelpie, ' and I will fight to the death rather than allow you in, until my bit is delivered up to me.'

' You don't frighten me,' said the bold John Macdonald, ' so you might as well calm down.' And he walked round to the back of the house, took out the bit from his pocket, lifted it high in the air, and hurled it in through his kitchen window. He then went back to the front, and told the infuriated Kelpie what he had done.

The Kelpie trotted swiftly round to the back, but above the back door was a cross, made from the wood of the sacred rowan tree. When the Kelpie saw this, it began to shudder and shake. Even its master, the Devil, would not have dared cross a threshold with such an emblem above the door. The animal trotted back to the front, and there stood John with his cudgel. The Kelpie at last admitted that it was beaten. It went off, its head lowered and its tail drooping, and disappeared into the mauve mists of the hills. That was the last anyone ever saw of this particular Kelpie.

John Macdonald resisted the temptation to look into the hole of the magic bridle. Having rid himself of the Kelpie, perhaps he wisely decided it was better not to be plagued by witches and fairies. He hid the bit, and told no-one of its hiding-place. Perhaps, one day, someone will come across it in the ruins of a cottage, or dig it up on a lonely moor, or fish it up from the depths of the Kelpie's own lake.

The Black Bodach ✎∾

IN a certain valley in Caithness, the people are known for their
kindness and hospitality, but there was one occasion when they
did not show themselves very hospitable, and suffered very much
as a consequence. And this was the way of it.

It was a year when winter came raging down the mountainside
before the autumn had had time to place one golden foot in the
valley. The crops had not fully ripened and lay, useless and frost-
bitten, in the fields. The people, whose sole livelihood was farm-
ing, had to tighten their belts, rely on the food and necessities
they had saved in past years, and wait with patience for a new
year to arrive, bringing with it new hope. In these circumstances,
perhaps they could scarcely be blamed for rejecting the stranger
who suddenly appeared in their midst. The big, dark, lazy-
looking fellow who swaggered one day into the valley had never
been seen before, refused to say from where he came, and
demanded food from every door at which he knocked. And at
every door he was turned away.

'Six mouths to feed here, and not enough to last us until
January,' he was told at one cottage.

'Go and find berries and nuts, for it's all you'll eat in this
valley,' he was told sharply at another cottage.

Finally, he arrived at the last house in the glen, the miller's
house.

'Have you anything to give a stranger to eat?' he asked the

43

miller's wife, who opened the door to him. ' A bite of bread, or
a piece of cheese, or perhaps a mug of milk ? '

' You'll get nothing here,' was the short reply.

The stranger glowered at her, and his bushy black eyebrows
met in a frown above his huge, hooked nose. He was tall as a
tree and thick as a tree trunk.

' Well, if I'll get nothing to eat,' he bellowed in a voice like
the rumblings of an earthquake, ' then the folk in this valley will
have little pleasure in their eating.'

The woman of the house, frightened not only by his threats
but by the appearance of the weird stranger, quickly shut the
door in his face. The stranger marched off to the mill itself and,
pushing aside the miller and his helpless assistants, he picked up
the mill-stone as if it were a piece of paper, put it on his shoulders,
and strode out of the valley.

Not long after this, the people began to miss some of their
cattle and sheep from the hills. At first, they were not worried,
accustomed as they were to occasional maraudings by fox or
eagle or stray dog. But, later, when money and valuables began
to disappear mysteriously from their homes, they were seriously
concerned. The men organised a day-and-night watch on their
stock. The women kept a constant look-out in their houses.
Everyone—men, women and children—kept an eye open for
suspicious-looking strangers, and particularly for the big, black
stranger who had robbed the miller of his mill-stone. No trace
of the robber could be found, and yet still the stealing continued.
Some of the men, in desperation, went to the ' wise woman ' of
the valley to seek advice.

' We have had worries enough this winter,' said their spokesman, ' without now having to battle with an invisible robber.'

' You say *invisible* robber,' mused the old woman. ' There

you have the secret. This thief, whoever he may be, is in league with the powers of the underworld, and therefore he is able to make himself invisible to ordinary human eyes. Your robber is the Black Bodach, the man who walked recently into this valley and was refused food at every door.'

' But we could not spare food for strangers ; we had scarcely sufficient for ourselves,' interrupted one of the men.

' I am not arguing the rights and wrongs of the case,' quavered the old woman. ' I am telling you the facts. The Black Bodach is your enemy, and a powerful enemy too. He fights with magic : you must fight back with magic.'

' What magic may we use ? ' asked another of the men. ' Tell us what we must do.'

' Choose a few of your number,' instructed the wise woman. ' I will lay a charm on them which will open their eyes to mysteries which have lain hidden. Then they will be able to see the Black Bodach when next he comes raiding.'

The bravest men of the valley volunteered for the job. The wise woman laid her charm upon them, and that night the picked band of men made its way to the hills, and stayed there, watching.

It was not long before they saw the Black Bodach come stalking down a hill. Not one of the men was brave enough to be the first to make a move. They watched silently as the Black Bodach fixed an arrow in his huge bow of ash, and released the bow-string. The arrow zoomed through the air and found its target in the flank of an unfortunate bullock. The Bodach moved over to the dead animal and, swinging it over his shoulders as easily as he had done the mill-stone, he made for the hill-top. The valley men now found energy to act, and, with fierce shouts and cries, they gave chase. The Bodach began to run,

45

and he ran fast and easily, as if the bullock on his shoulders were but the collar of his coat. But the valley men were fleet of foot too, and, whereas the Bodach had already come some distance, they were fresh and rested after their period of waiting and watching. They had nearly caught up to him—indeed, they were near enough to hear the sound of his heavy breathing—when a gauzy, grey mist descended suddenly, like a curtain, between the men and their quarry. They stayed where they were until the mist rolled away, by which time there was no sign of the Black Bodach.

The men went back miserably to the valley to report what had happened.

' Don't worry,' said the oldest inhabitant, ' at least you *saw* the Black Bodach. At least, we know the charm worked well on you.'

' There will be other chances,' said the miller. ' I suggest that you have all the food and drink you require so that you may be strong and ready for the Bodach the next time he appears.'

The charmed band welcomed this suggestion. They felt themselves to be something of heroes, and they were quite happy to undertake the task of watching and waiting for the Bodach to appear again.

He did appear : again and again and again. And each time he stole a bullock or a sheep ; and each time the men gave chase ; and each time they lost the robber in a suddenly falling mist.

As time went on, the men and women who stayed in the valley began to whisper among themselves. Surely the Black Bodach should have been captured by now. The charmed men had had chances enough. Although mists were frequent on the hill-top, it was odd that they should fall so suddenly and so conveniently for the Bodach. Perhaps the watchers were foiled in their attempts to capture the robber, not because of mountain mists but because of the large amount of ' mountain dew '—or whiskey—they consumed.

When this gossip came to the ears of the picked band of men, they decided that something must be done to prevent the further blackening of their reputations. One of them had heard of an old woman living in Sutherland who, it was said, had a brother who lived somewhere in their own district. Since it was also said that this old woman was a witch, what more likely than that the Black Bodach was that brother? So to the old woman the men went, told their story, and demanded that she should tell them how they might prevent the mist falling when next they were in pursuit of her brother.

' He's no brother of mine,' denied the old crone indignantly. ' I don't know what you're blethering about.'

The men insisted, and when they threatened to have her burnt as a witch if she didn't help them, she gave them the advice they needed.

' I still deny, mind you, that he's my brother,' she said. ' All the same, I can tell you the exact time to choose for following the Black Bodach. Watch for him on the seventh day of the seventh month, and then no mist will fall between him and you. Now, away with you : I've no more to say.'

On the seventh day of the seventh month, the men were duly on the look-out. The Bodach appeared, shot his usual prey and, with his usual confidence, ran towards the hill-top with his pursuers after him. This time, the mist did not fall between them. The frightened Bodach put on speed, and made for his den which was not far away. The men followed, and were surprised to see that he had set up the mill-stone at the outer door of his dwelling. As they closed round it, they could hear the dark stranger muttering charms inside, but these proved useless, for no further mist came down between the robber and his enemies.

The Bodach decided to fight : he began to shoot arrows fast and thick through the hole of the mill-stone. The pursuers bravely closed up together and stood shoulder to shoulder, ready to make a dash forward. The Bodach emerged very suddenly from behind the mill-stone, and raced away swiftly over the mountain. The men, of course, should have followed him immediately, but something in the den caught their eyes, and curiosity prompted them to enter and look around. Stacked around the walls of the simply constructed dwelling-place was such wealth as the rajahs of India might envy. While they were congratulating each other on this glorious find, one of them pointed out that their only chance of enjoying the spoil was to slay the Bodach. If they took away the gold, silver and jewels while he was still alive, he would only steal it back again. So they marked the spot with an arrow stuck on a slight rising near by. The thought of the treasure that might be theirs gave extra speed to their feet, and they eagerly chased after the Black Bodach. They ran a distance of three or four miles before they came in sight of him, and, even then, although they aimed a few well-directed shots at him, the arrows seemed to glance off his body as if it were made of stone. They were about to give up in despair when, as luck would have it, the Bodach stumbled and fell over a hair trip-rope which had been placed there many weeks before for this very purpose. He was soon overtaken and killed.

The men scarcely waited to rest their tired limbs. They turned round and directed their steps back to the Bodach's den. They found the spot where they had placed the arrow, but could see no mill-stone nor any den. The men scattered, and continued the search. Some went one way, some another. Every group found another arrow. A wider search revealed several hundred arrows, each similar to the one they had stuck on the hillock a few hours earlier. They searched until nightfall, and then returned home to tell the tale of their success with the killing of the Bodach and their disappointment over their failure to find the treasure.

The next day every inhabitant of the valley turned out to look for the mill-stone, the Bodach's den and the treasure. Although the guides were certain as to where the mill-stone was last seen, none of them now could see it, and no-one ever saw the treasure again. The Black Bodach was dead, but his magic lived on after him.

To this day, there are holiday-makers who visit the district, people who have never heard the tale of the Black Bodach. They climb the mountains, and when they return to the valley where they are staying, they ask why there should be a mill-stone way up in the hills where no mill has ever been. The story is then told them, and eagerly they volunteer to lead a party to the spot. But it so happens that those who have seen it once, and heard the legend once, can never see the mill-stone again. And many a party of eager hunters has searched up and down and round and about the hill-sides, but the treasure remains where it is—and where it probably always will—in a fairy spot hidden from human eye.

The Tale of the Three Brothers ❧

THERE was once a farmer who had three sons, and on the birthday of each son, he planted a tree in his garden. And when each tree had grown a little, he carved on the trunk the name of the boy for whom it was planted. The tallest tree had ' Colin ' cut in the bark ; the next tree had ' Hamish ' on it ; and the smallest tree was marked with ' Charles '.

One day Charles was playing under the shade of his particular tree when he heard some music in the distance. He stopped what he was doing, and listened. The music was very sweet, and he wondered who could be playing. One of his brothers had a flute, but Charles had never heard him play anything on it but wrong notes, and he wasn't even sure that the instrument he heard now was the flute. He started to walk in the direction from which the music came, and his dog, a devoted companion, left his bone and followed him.

The nearer Charles came to the source of the music, the sweeter it sounded. Like one enchanted, he followed the sound all afternoon until he was far from home, in countryside that was unfamiliar to him. It grew dark : Charles grew frightened. He was only a young lad, and had never travelled alone this far before. To his relief, he saw ahead of him the glimmer of a light. He could hear the music no longer, so was able to concentrate his efforts on reaching the spot where the light made a tiny yellow circle in the blackness. When he reached it, he found it came

from the window of a small house. He knocked on the door.
There was no reply so, lifting the latch, he went in. The little
house was deserted, although it was well lit by candles, and there
was a roaring fire in the hearth.

The boy and his dog were warming themselves by the fire
when there came a knock at the door. The dog sprang up, placed
himself protectively in front of his young master, and started to
growl.

' It's all right, old fellow,' whispered Charles, putting his hand
on the dog's shaggy head. ' We mustn't be frightened.'

For all that, Charles himself was a little scared, and it was in a
shaking voice that he called out, ' Who's there ? '

A voice outside replied, ' Let me in ; I am your first cousin.'

Charles knew all his cousins well, and didn't recognise this
voice as belonging to any of them.

' Whoever you are, I cannot let you in,' he called back.

' I am able to come in by the smallest hole you can make,'
came the reply.

' I'm not going to make any hole for you, so there ! ' shouted
Charles, sounding much braver than he felt.

' Oh, yes, you will ! ' was the forceful answer. ' There is a
hammer and a nail on the mantelpiece, and you must make a
hole with them.'

Charles didn't want to obey these instructions, but something
impelled him to do so. He was drawn against his will towards
the mantelpiece, and the same force made him drive the nail
through the door, and then pull it out to leave the hole open. He
returned to replace hammer and nail, and when he looked
round, there was nothing there but a harmless hen, scuffing about
on the floor. It looked much too big to have got through the
tiny hole he had made, yet the door was still shut. Charles was

amazed. He was still more amazed when the hen spoke to him. ' Tie up that dog,' it said. ' I don't like the look of him. Tie up that dog, and be quick about it. See, here is a string.'

Again rather against his will, the lad did as he was told. The hen came up close to the fire, and, after a few minutes, began to grow bigger and bigger and bigger.

' You are growing,' said Charles, in wonderment.

' No, I am not ! ' said the hen. ' It is only my feathers fluffing out in the warmth of the fire.'

In a few more minutes, the boy spoke again. ' You are certainly growing now.'

' Yes,' agreed the hen. ' And you had better take care of yourself.'

At this, the hen's feathers began to change into short-haired hide, horns appeared on its head, the short feathery tail lengthened into a long, swishing one. The hen had changed into a small bull and, charging at Charles, began to fight him. The boy called out to his dog for assistance, but the bull shouted, ' Tighten, rope, tighten ! ' And the string round the dog's neck grew thick and strong as the bull called out, and the dog was held back.

After a brief struggle, poor Charles was overcome. The bull pushed his body into a barrel and covered it with salt.

The boy's father was worried when his youngest son did not return that night, and in the morning, when he looked out of his bedroom window and saw that Charles's little tree had fallen to the ground, he at once supposed that his son was dead. And there was great sorrow in the house.

A few days later, Hamish was lying under his tree, reading a book, when he, too, heard sweet music. As Charles had done, he arose and followed the sound. He was eager to get nearer to the music, but could not. When it grew dark, the music stopped.

The hen had changed into a small bull

He also entered the small house as his brother had done, and met with the same fate.

When his middle son did not return that night, the farmer was worried, and in the morning, when he looked out of his bedroom window and saw that Hamish's medium-sized tree had fallen to the ground, he at once supposed that his son was dead. And there was great sorrow in the house.

The eldest son said to his father, ' Father, I must go and find my brothers.'

' Alas, Colin,' said the farmer, ' I am sure that they are dead.'

' Then I must find their bodies,' said Colin, ' that we may give them decent Christian burial.'

For hours he searched without success the fields, the ditches, the valleys and the hills. Then, as night fell, he saw a tiny, flickering light where earlier there had been no sign of habitation. He approached and entered the house, his dog following closely at

53

his heels. Colin thought he heard his dog whining, and stooped to soothe him. The dog looked up at him inquiringly.

' Was it not you that whined, then ? ' asked Colin softly. He looked slowly round the room, and there he saw his brothers' two dogs, nearly dead with hunger, thick ropes around their necks. He cut the ropes, gave them some of the meat he had brought with him, and told them to stay hidden in a dark corner of the room.

He crossed to the fire to warm himself. There was a knock at the door.

' Come in, whoever you are,' said Colin cheerfully.

The hen strutted in, and immediately ordered him to tie up the dog. It handed Colin a piece of string, but the young man, wiser than his younger brothers, used a string of his own to tie up the dog, and, secretly, threw the other piece into the fire. Also, he tied the string loosely so that, when the dog tugged, it could easily slip off him.

The usual talk followed. The hen grew bigger and bigger and bigger until it changed into a bull, and prepared to attack its victim.

Colin whistled to the three dogs.

' Tighten, rope, tighten,' grunted the bull. But the three dogs attacked. Charles's dog seized the bull's tail ; Hamish's dog seized one of its paws ; and Colin's dog leapt on its back. It wasn't long before the bull saw that it was outwitted. It bellowed for mercy. Colin called off the dogs, and tied up the bull.

' Now, you wretched animal,' he said, ' tell me what you have done with my brothers.'

' They are in salt in the two barrels over there,' replied the bull.

' And how may I rescue them ? ' demanded Colin.

'Strike the barrels with the switch that hangs behind the door, and they will jump out,' replied the bull.

'And have you anything else to tell me?' asked Colin, in a threatening voice.

'Yes, yes,' said the bull. 'There are three kegs of gold hidden under the floor—one for each of you—and there is a small knife in the wall that will do anything you tell it.'

As you may have guessed, Colin was a quick-witted young man.

'Little knife, little knife,' he said, 'come and cut off this beast's head.'

The knife obeyed.

The two brothers were then awakened from their salty sleep, and they rejoiced greatly at the reunion. They found the kegs of gold under the floor boards, and, after a few hours' sleep, the three of them set off on the long journey home.

The farmer was greatly worried when his eldest son did not return that night, and, in the morning, he scarce dared to look out of his bedroom window lest he see the tallest tree had fallen to the ground. At last, he forced himself to look, and there, in the garden, he saw, to his delight, that all three trees were standing, graceful and upright. He knew then that his sons were alive.

In the afternoon, the sons came home, each with his keg of gold, and each spent many hours recounting to the farmer the story of his adventure. When they counted the gold, they found they had enough money to keep them in comfort until the end of their days.

The Witch of Laggan 〰

WITCHES were sometimes a nuisance, and sometimes even a danger, and, so powerful was their command of magic, it took a brave man to fight them. Murray the hunter was such a man. Whenever a witch committed any evil deed in his district, Murray sought her out and punished her. The witches regarded him as the greatest of their enemies. This is the tale of how one of them tried to wreak vengeance, and of how she failed to do so.

Murray was out hunting. He had had a hard, and not very successful day, and was making his way home when a storm arose. The black clouds met and banged together in resounding drum-rolls, while the lightning zigzagged across the mountains and lit up the shivering dogs as they followed their master down the mountainside. Then the rain began to pour down in huge sheets of water. Murray decided to seek shelter. He found a little stone bothy that his friend, the shepherd, sometimes used when the sheep were lambing and he had to stay the night on the hills.

There was a fire laid in the hearth, which Murray lit, and soon he and the dogs were drying themselves in front of the comforting flames. The hunter was sharing with his dogs some bread and meat his good wife had put in his pocket for him, when there was a little scratching noise at the door. The dogs leapt to their feet.

56

'Lie down, lie down,' coaxed Murray. 'There is nothing to be frightened about.'

But the hounds would not be quietened, and one of them started to whimper. The scratching came again, followed by a faint 'Miaouw!'

'There, you see,' said Murray, smiling at his dogs. 'It's only a cat which wants shelter, like us. Shall I let it in?'

The dogs growled their disapproval at the suggestion, but Murray went to the door and opened it. Into the bothy walked a jet-black cat, with a long bushy tail and green eyes that glittered like emeralds. At the sight of the cat, the dogs became more restless, growling and showing their teeth. She, however, ignored them and, padding gracefully across the floor, settled herself in front of the fire.

'Just a wee pussy,' said Murray, putting out a hand to tickle a jet-black ear.

The dogs retreated into a corner and there they stood, tails down and teeth still bared. Now, Murray had a couple of cats at home, and his dogs were very friendly with them. It was unusual for them to behave like this, yet, however hard Murray tried, they refused to be pacified.

'I wish you dogs could speak and tell me what is worrying you,' he said. 'There's something odd here.'

The dogs started to bark and howl, and Murray decided he must turn out the cat. He opened the door.

'Shoo! Shoo!' he said to her.

The cat arose slowly from the hearth, and fixed its great green eyes upon the hunter.

'Are you really a cat, an *ordinary* cat, I wonder?' mused Murray.

'Miaouw, miaouw!' mewed the cat. Then, to Murray's

surprise, she spoke in a human voice. ' You are right to wonder, Murray the Hunter,' she said. ' I am not an ordinary cat. I am a witch.'

On hearing this, Murray backed away from her in alarm.

' Do not be frightened,' said the cat-that-was-a-witch. ' I intend you no harm. Indeed, if you will shelter me this stormy night, I promise to give up my wicked ways, and shall become an ordinary good wife of Laggan.'

After some thought, Murray agreed to her request.

' But before I'll sit down again,' continued the cat, ' I'll thank you to tie up your hounds for, to tell you the truth, I don't much like the look of them, and they certainly don't appear to like the look of me.'

Murray said that he would do this but that, unfortunately, he had nothing with which to tie them up. The cat then mysteriously produced a hair rope. Perhaps it was this that made Murray suddenly suspicious. At any rate, although he went over to the corner where the hounds were still whimpering, instead of tying the rope to the dogs, he tied it around one of the beams that supported the roof of the bothy.

He and the cat sat by the fire, and as time went on, the cat began to change her shape, and slowly took on her true appearance. When, finally, the four paws of the cat merged into the two feet of the witch, she leapt up from the fireside.

' Now, Murray the Hunter,' she hissed, ' your time has come. Long enough have you persecuted me and mine. Vengeance is at hand.' Uttering curses at him in her wild witch's voice, she flew at his throat.

' Help me, my dogs, help me ! ' called out Murray.

' Your dogs are tied up,' cackled the witch, ' and they, too, shall die. Tighten, rope, tighten.'

' Now, Murray the Hunter, your time has come '

But, of course, the rope didn't tighten itself around the hounds as the witch expected it would. It tightened itself around the beam. The dogs leapt at the witch ; the beam began to crack. And the witch knew she had been deceived. The dogs sank their teeth into her, and shook her to and fro. She kicked and hit at them. They didn't let go until, suddenly, she changed back into a cat, sank her sharp claws into them, and managed to make her escape.

The storm was over, and Murray and his dogs hurried home. The hunter's wife was at the door to greet them. She was dressed in her outdoor clothes.

' Where are you going ? ' asked Murray.

' Nowhere,' replied his wife. ' I have just returned. I have been to see the Good Wife of Laggan who lies mortally ill in her cottage. There is nothing I can do for her.'

Leaving the dogs with his wife, Murray made his way to the dwelling-place of the so-called ' Good Wife of Laggan '. He found her lying on her bed, and, when she saw him, she gave one loud shriek—and died.

As far as Murray was concerned, that was the end of the story. But a tale is told in the district of how, that very night, two travellers met a blood-stained woman running in the direction of a churchyard with two black dogs chasing her. A few minutes later, they met a fierce-looking black man astride a black horse. The man reined in his horse and asked, in a deep, black voice, ' Have you seen a woman pass this way with two black dogs at her heels ? '

The travellers agreed that they had.

' There is a churchyard not far away in this direction, is there not ? ' asked the black man.

The travellers said there was.

' Could the woman be in the holy ground of the churchyard before the dogs caught her, do you think ? ' asked the black man.

The travellers said she might, and the black man rode away.

A little later, the travellers were overtaken by this same horseman. Lying across the horse's back, in front of the rider, was the Witch of Laggan. On her body were not only the marks made by Murray's dogs but also those made by the mysterious black dogs of the horseman. Thus, it was said, was the Witch of Laggan claimed by her master, the Devil.

The Wizard of Reay's Book of Magic ᘑ☙

A CERTAIN Donald Mackay once lived in the north of
Sutherland, and, because of his great powers of magic, he
was known as the Wizard of Reay. Donald had few possessions,
but the one he prized most highly was his Book of Magic.
One day, he promised to lend this book to a friend and neighbour who, like himself, was something of a magician. He called
his servant to him.

'Take this precious book,' he said, 'to the man who visited
here last week, and who lives at the other end of the valley. The
journey will take you some time, and you need not hurry. But
one thing you must promise me : whatever you do, do not open
this and attempt to read it on the way.'

The servant promised, and set out on the journey. He
walked briskly for a few miles, but the heat of the noonday sun
and the weight of the big Book of Magic soon made him weary.
He sat down in the warm bracken at the bottom of a hill, and
began to eat his lunch of home-made bread and goat's-milk
cheese. When he had finished his meal, he rested. His eyes
wandered over the cover of the mysterious book.

'I'd dearly love to know what powerful information it
contains,' he said to himself.

His hand strayed towards the book but, withdrawing it
quickly, he murmured, ' No, no, I must not : did I not promise
my master that I would not open it ? '

He closed his eyes, and went to sleep. He dreamt that he was as powerful as his master and the envy of all his friends ; he dreamt that he commanded the fortunes of the world ; he dreamt that all the fairies in creation were his servants, ready to obey his every whim. And when he awoke, he could resist temptation no longer. His curiosity overcame him ; he picked up the book, and started to turn over its pages. He scarcely knew what he read ; he knew only that in less than a few seconds he was surrounded by hundreds and hundreds of little men. The air was loud with their clamour.

' Work ! ' they cried. ' Give us work ! '

The servant did not know what to say to this, and stayed silent until the cries became more insistent and even a little threatening.

' Work ! Work ! Work ! '

His ears were deafened by the chanting. He realised that he had brought this trouble on himself by breaking the promise he had made to his master, but it was too late now ; he must think of something to occupy these noisy little men, something that would take them a long, long time so that he would not be bothered by them again. He had an idea.

' All right,' he said, ' I'll give you work. See the heather that lies all around us. Turn every bit of it into ropes.'

The ground was thick with purple heather as far as the eye could see. The servant was sure that the task was an impossible one. In a flash, the little men had swarmed over the moors and hill-sides. They worked at such speed that the servant was made quite dizzy watching them. And he had had scarcely time to get to his feet, when they dragged towards him mile upon mile of heather rope. Their task was completed.

' Work ! Work ! More work ! ' shrieked the little men.

The servant was beside himself with worry, but, again, his quick wits came to his aid. He had another idea.

'All right,' he said, 'I'll give you work. Go to the Bay of Tongue, to the seashore. Fashion me ropes out of the sand you will find there.'

Off rushed the armies of little men. But even the fairies have their limitations. They may be able to make ropes from heather, but they cannot make ropes from sand. They spent a long time trying and, when at last they failed completely, their wrath was turned against the man who had set them such an impossible task. They decided that never again should their labour be available to whoever opened the Book of Magic. They left the district that very day, and were never seen there again.

The servant returned to his master, and confessed what he had done. He never forgot the anger with which Donald Mackay greeted this confession; neither did he forget Donald's final forgiveness of his disobedience. The Wizard of Reay was a great man and a good master. Although he lost for ever the assistance of his fairies, he never mentioned the matter again to his servant. And it was said that he did not lose all his powers of magic : by the merest wave of his hand he could still bring down rain or hail or snow from the heavens.

Luran and the Fairies ❧

ONCE upon a time there lived a farmer called Luran, Son of the Dark Man, and Luran had a herd of cattle of which he was very proud. One morning, when he went to the fields to drive the cows to the shed for milking, he noticed that one of them was missing. He was not unduly worried by this : he thought she had strayed and would probably turn up some time later in the day. Nightfall came, and still the cow was missing, and the next morning another cow had gone. Each morning for a week, Luran counted his herd, and each morning he found he had lost another cow. His large herd was gradually turning into a small herd, and, if matters went on like this, he would soon have no cows left. Luran decided to keep an eye on them for a night or two, in the hope of solving the mystery of their disappearance.

He hid in a ditch, and waited. Soon after midnight, he heard some commotion coming from a hillock at the far end of his field. It was a moonlit night, and he saw clearly the side of the hillock open and a band of little people stream out. The fairies—for such they were—surrounded one of Luran's cows and began to urge it, with cries and shouts, towards their hillock home. Luran made a quick decision. If he wanted to find out exactly what was happening to his cows, he must join the fairies and hope they would not notice him in the crowd.

He crept across the field, and mingled with the thieves. The

64

cow, hearing Luran's voice amongst the rest, meekly trotted as she was bid towards the fairies' home, followed by the fairy thieves and Luran himself. Inside the hill, Luran watched his cow being killed and skinned. He dared not speak against this, but stayed quietly where he was, in the shadows of the wall. The fairies cooked some steaks of the beef, and sat down to a good meal. There was much laughing, joking and singing. After they had eaten, the fairies began to nod and yawn, and Luran watched them fall asleep, one by one. Soon the hillock was silent but for the occasional snore and grunt of a sleeping fairy.

Many precious goblets stood on the fairies' dining table. Luran eyed these, wondering if it would be right for him to take away some of them. After all, it would only be fair compensation for the cows he had lost. Or would it be ? Possibly one goblet would be worth more than a herd of cows. He looked around him, and there on the fire he saw a large copper kettle. He thought it would be fair to take this in return for his cows, and the fairies might still have had the better of the bargain. He tip-toed over to it, and lifted it off the fire. Then he carefully stepped between the bodies of the sleepers, and made for the entrance of the hillock. As he went through the doorway, the kettle accident-ally banged against the side. *Clang ! Clang !* The noise resounded through the room. The fairies woke up with a start. Luran started to run across the field. He had scarcely reached the gate before sixteen of the fairies were in hot pursuit.

Luran raced through the gate—after him raced the fairies. Over a ditch leapt Luran—over the ditch leapt the fairies. Through heather and bracken scrambled Luran—through heather and bracken scrambled the fairies. Luran began to breathe heavily with exhaustion, but the fairies seemed as fresh as when they had left their hillock. Luran turned his head to see how far

65

behind they were, and found they had gained on him by several yards. He might have run more freely, had he thrown away the copper kettle, but he clung on to it determinedly. On he ran— on ran the fairies. They had nearly caught up with him, when he heard a mysterious voice call :

' Luran, Son of the Black One,
Get thee among the black stones by the shore.'

This reminded him that fairies are frightened of the sea, and will not venture on the seashore below high-tide mark. He changed his course, and ran towards the beach. The sea was out, and there was a line of dark rocks high on the shore, beyond which the tide never came. Luran clambered over them and collapsed, exhausted, on the sand. The sixteen fairies danced with rage on the rocks, but none ventured farther. They knew they were beaten, and they must have recognised a dauntless foe in Luran, for they never bothered him again, nor touched his cows. And they let him keep the fairy kettle which boiled water in less time than it took to fill and which, together with his cows, Luran prized more highly than anything else on earth.

How Mackay First Brought Fire into the World ❦

IN the long, long ago there lived a Highlander called Mackay, and, one cold winter day, his wife came to him and said :

' Mackay, you and I would be a deal warmer if you could make us a fire.'

And Mackay went and found two bits of stick, and began to rub them together.

' You're taking a long time about it, Mackay,' chided his wife, ' and in the meantime I am getting colder and colder and colder.'

Mackay rubbed away with his two bits of stick until his arms ached with weariness, but not a spark did he strike.

' Can't you hurry, man ? ' urged his wife.

' Hold your tongue, woman,' said Mackay. ' Am I not doing the best I can ? '

At last, made desperate by his failure, Mackay began to curse. He dropped the sticks and, seeing the look of displeasure on his wife's face, he went away to the hills. He had not gone far—and his temper had greatly improved by now—when he saw a golden ball of fire rolling over the moor.

' Why, there's a glorious sight,' said Mackay to himself. ' If only I could catch that, what a lot of bother it would save me.'

He ran across the moor, leaping ditches, wading through brooks, pushing through bracken. The ball of fire was always just ahead of him. A hill seemed about to stop it going farther, but the golden ball mysteriously rolled *up* it. Mackay ran around the hill and, when the ball rolled down the other side, he was at the bottom, ready to catch it.

He put it in his pocket, and returned home to his wife.

' No need to eat any more raw meat,' he told her. ' From now on, we shall be able to have it roast.'

She was delighted, kissed him, and promised never to scold him again.

Between them, they kept the fire going. Neighbours from far and wide came to borrow light from it. Their neighbours, in turn, borrowed from them. Before long the precious gift of fire had spread throughout the world. And that is why the Clan Mackay to this day call themselves the ' Sons of Fire '.

The Silver Chanter of the MacCrimmons

IAIN Og MacCrimmon sat on a mound near his home at Borreraig in the west of Skye, and sighed so loudly that the grass was ruffled at his feet. A competition was being held at Dunvegan Castle to find a man skilled enough to be appointed hereditary piper to MacLeod of MacLeod. Iain was a piper, but he had not been considered good enough even to attend the competition, which was why he sighed. Now, a fairy chanced to hear that sigh, and found it in her heart to be sorry for Iain Og MacCrimmon. She tripped up to him, and asked why he was sad, and, when he had explained the reason to her, she said to him, 'I have heard you playing, and I find your music sweet enough. You are a handsome young man, and the sight of you pleases me. I will do something for you.'

Iain knew that a fairy can change the white water of the rill into rich wine, that she can weave the threads of the spider into a tartan plaid, and that she can bring the music of the lull of repose and peace from the stalk of a fairy reed, so he knew that this was an important moment in his life. He thanked her gravely, and waited to see what would happen. In a few minutes she produced a silver chanter, which is the tube with finger-holes that is used in the bagpipe.

'Take this,' she said. 'With the touch of your fingers, it will always bring forth the sweetest music, and it will do the same for your sons and your sons' sons and their sons, and for all

69

generations of MacCrimmons to come. But the Silver Chanter must be cared for and treated with reverence, as it is a fairy gift. If the day should come when a MacCrimmon neglects or insults it, the gift of piping which I bestow on you shall be taken away for all time.'

Iain Og took the Chanter, and hastened away to Dunvegan. There collected the most famous pipers from all over the Highlands. One by one they played the music that their forefathers had played before them. And each was more skilled than the last. When Iain Og's turn came, he fitted the Silver Chanter to his bagpipes, and began to play. There was a hushed silence among the listening crowds. Such piping as this had never been heard before. Iain's playing was enchanting, and his bagpipes truly enchanted. He knew, without being told, that there was no doubt that he would be chosen as hereditary piper to MacLeod of MacLeod. And so it was. The judges recognised that here was a piper who had the gift of fairy fingers on the chanter.

From that day on, the MacCrimmons of Skye produced many generations of famous pipers and composers of pipe-music. Shortly after the Silver Chanter came into their possession, they founded a piping-college at Borreraig, and pupils from all parts of Scotland and Ireland came to this college. The course was a long one ; it is said that it takes seven years to learn to be a piper, and that, to be a really good one, a piper must have had seven generations of pipers in his family before him.

The centuries went by, and still the MacCrimmons were pipers to the MacLeods, until there came a day which proved to be a fatal one in their history.

The Chief of the MacLeods was returning home to Skye from the nearby island of Raasay. The piper's seat was at the prow of the chief's galley, and, in that seat, sat MacCrimmon. It was a windy day, and there was a great swell on the sea. Up and down, up and down, swung the galley in the churning waters. 'Play us a tune, MacCrimmon, to keep up our spirits,' ordered the Chief.

MacCrimmon put his fingers to the famous Silver Chanter. As he played, the swelling of the waters increased, and, every now and again, skilled though his fingers were, they slipped from the chanter when the swinging of the galley proved too much for them. The spray from one huge wave hit MacCrimmon a stinging blow in the face, causing him to play a few wrong notes. No member of the MacCrimmon family had ever played a wrong note on the pipes. This particular MacCrimmon laid down his bagpipes in disgust, and forgot the instructions that the fairy donor had given Iain Og so long ago, although his father had often told him the story.

'This wretched Silver Chanter!' he exclaimed in the heat of the moment. 'How can any piper expect to get a decent note out of it!'

As soon as he had spoken, he regretted his words. He knew, in his heart, that his remarks had been unjust. It was too late: the Silver Chanter arose of its own accord, and slipped over the edge of the boat into the foaming green sea.

The spell was broken. MacCrimmon found he could no longer play the pipes skilfully, neither could his sons nor his sons' sons. The fame of the MacCrimmon piping-college soon died away, and the college itself finally fell into decay. The ghosts of the ancient pipers alone were left to pipe their magic airs in the deserted caverns and on the windy cliffs of Borreraig, with only the sea-birds for audience.

The Little One 〜➤

ONCE upon a time a family called Mackay lived in Kintyre, and a Brownie lived with them who was known through the countryside as the Little One. Now, Brownies, as you probably know, are little men, brothers to the fairies, curly-headed and wrinkled of face. The Highland Brownie has always been regarded with love and respect. They used to take up residence in castles or big houses, and take upon themselves all sorts of domestic duties, and, as long as they were not annoyed or upset, they were very useful members of the household.

The Little One had lived with the Mackays for a long time. When a certain Colonel Mackay went off to the Peninsular War in 1812, it was said that the Little One accompanied him. The Colonel came through many fierce battles without as much as a scratch. He could be seen riding into battle, the Little One perched in front of him on the peak of his saddle, and, as the bullets showered about him, the Brownie warded them off. When the war ended, he returned to Kintyre with the Colonel, and took up his residence again in the Mackay house, applying himself to his usual jobs of cleaning and scrubbing and tidying. He added to these the new duty of keeping his master's uniform in good condition, brushing it carefully every day, and polishing the buttons. And he might be with the Mackay family to this day were it not for the unfortunate fact that Colonel Mackay decided to marry a Sassenach.

' I'll leave them for good, that's what I'll do '

Brownies like to do their work at night, and every morning, just before daybreak, the Little One left the house, always letting himself out by the back door. He probably returned to his own folk for the hours of daylight. One wintry night, when the snow was thick upon the ground, Colonel Mackay was returning home from visiting a neighbour's house, when he saw some tiny footprints in the snow. He dismounted from his horse, and examined them. They were the footprints the Little One had made on his return to the Mackay house that evening. And the footprints were bloodstained.

Mackay hastened home, and spoke to his wife.

' My dear, I am worried about the Little One,' he said. ' Tonight I saw his footsteps in the snow, and they were bloodstained. The poor little chap is walking about barefoot in this terrible weather, and his feet are obviously badly cut as a result. He has done so much for us that we must do something for him. Will you look out a pair of shoes, and put them where he can easily find them ? '

His wife said she would, but she was a Sassenach and did not know how easily a Highland Brownie takes offence. She was a busy housewife, and picked up the first pair of shoes that came to hand, a shabby pair belonging to one of her children. She knew her husband had intended the Brownie to have a good pair, but, 'Why waste good shoes on a Brownie?' she asked herself. 'These will do. They're not much use to anyone else, and I haven't time to look for another pair.'

She left the shoes on a flagstone at the back door where the Little One would be sure to see them when he arrived the next night. And the Brownie certainly did see them. In fact, he nearly tripped over them in the dark. He knew at once that they were meant for him, but when he took them into the light and saw how old and shabby they were, he hopped around the kitchen in rage, screaming and cursing.

'If this is all they think of me,' he screeched, in his funny squeaky voice, 'they can well do without me. I'll leave them! I'll leave them for good, that's what I'll do.'

And that's exactly what he did.

The Brownie of Rothiemurchus

ANOTHER Brownie whose valuable services were lost through his master's thoughtlessness was one who lived in the household of the Grants at Rothiemurchus. This Brownie worked and worked, day long and night long, never needing sleep, and never asking for reward, apart from a daily supply of cream. During the day he helped the maids with their dusting and cleaning; at night, when everyone had gone to bed, he busied himself with cleaning the pots and pans, tidying up the fireplaces and removing the soot from the chimneys. Visitors to the house often wondered why their sleep was disturbed by the noise of clattering and clanking downstairs. Members of the household, who were accustomed to the noise, usually managed to sleep through it. But one night a Laird of Rothiemurchus, who was perhaps a lighter sleeper than his forefathers had been, made an unfortunate move. He was wakened from his sleep by the familiar rattlings and tinkerings.

'Oh, that Brownie!' he groaned, and turned over in the bed. There was silence for a few moments then, as he was dozing off, there it was again. *Bang! Clatter! Clang!* He sat up in bed. There was silence. He lay down again. The noise recommenced. The Brownie was working very hard this night.

The Laird got out of bed, and put on his dressing gown. By now, lack of sleep had made him bad-tempered and irritable. He groped his way to the top of the stairs. The Brownie was apparently busy on the pots and pans, and, from the sound of it, had dropped the lot on the stone floor of the kitchen.

' Hey, you Brownie ! ' called out the Laird peevishly.

The Brownie was making too much noise to hear his master's voice.

' Stop that dreadful din,' yelled the Laird, ' and let decent folk sleep.'

This time the Brownie heard him. There was tense silence from the kitchen. The Laird went back to his bedroom, got into his bed, and fell asleep. There was no more noise to disturb him that night.

The next morning, the maids found that the Brownie had left his work half-done. Dirty pots and pans were strewn over the kitchen. The fire-places were untouched and full of the dead ashes from the night before. The hearths were dirty and un-washed. The soot was thick in the chimneys.

The Laird never had his sleep disturbed again, as the Brownie never returned to help his household. Occasionally, milk and cream would disappear from the dairy, and it was suspected that the Brownie was the thief, but no-one ever saw him again.

The Oystercatcher, the Duck and the Hen ⤐

IT is said that, in days long ago, the lovely oystercatcher, found
on the shingly places near the shore or on the wild cliff-tops,
was a pure black bird. A tale is told in the West Highlands of
how Christ was once pursued by His enemies through the
Hebridean islands, and, as He was running along the seashore,
two oystercatchers saw Him.

' He needs help,' said one of the birds.

' He shall have it,' replied the other.

Then they bade Him lie down on the beach, and they covered
Him with seaweed, and kept watch over Him until His enemies
had passed. And while they were watching, they called out to
Him in their shrill notes, ' *Pic pic, pic pic*'—take care, take care.

The oystercatcher was rewarded with the gift of white
plumage on its breast for this loving attention to Our Lord, and
to this day, when the bird is in flight, you may see the snowy
feathers spread out like a white cross.

Another folk tale is told of how Christ was helped by a
crofter. His enemies were still pursuing Him when He came to a
croft where the crofter was winnowing the chaff from his corn.

As the oystercatcher had said, so the crofter murmured to
himself, ' He needs help,' adding, as the other oystercatcher had
done, ' and He shall have it.'

So he hid Christ under the heap of corn that he was winnowing. But it was a small heap, and scarcely covered Him, so, to

make Him safer until His enemies had passed, the crofter went to collect more corn from his barn near by. While he was gone, the poultry—ducks and hens—took advantage of his absence to feast on the heap of corn. The ducks merely trampled on the corn, eating as they trampled. But the hens, who must always scratch and scatter, spread the corn about the yard. When the crofter returned from his barn, he saw that the hens had exposed Christ to view. And, since the hens had so betrayed Him, it is said that from that day on, all hens and their chicks were made afraid of rain and snow, of sleet and wind, of thunder and lightning. It was also decreed that the hen's bath should be of dust and not of water, that she should have no oil for the proud preening of her feathers, and that her only joy should be that of dry land.

But, with the duck who had not scattered the grain, it was different. From that day on, the ducks and their ducklings were web-toed, they exulted in rain and snow, in sleet and wind, in thunder and lightning. The duck's bath was of water, she had oil for the proud preening of her feathers, and there were four joys of her life : the joy of land, the joy of water, the joy of under-water, and the joy of air.

So that, when the hen is at her saddest, the duck is at her happiest; when the hen is most despairing, the duck is most hopeful; when the hen is most frightened, the duck is most joyful. There is even an old Gaelic saying that bears out this legend : ' You are as happy as a duck expecting thunder.'

The Fox and the Wolf and the Keg of Butter ✺➧

A FOX and a wolf once lived together in a den in the dark forest. They hunted together, ate together and talked together, and they were supposed to be friends.

One day, they left their forest and found their way to the seashore. The night before, a boat had been wrecked on some treacherous rocks that were just submerged under the sea, and some of the ship's cargo had been thrown up on the beach. The two animals nosed their way through lengths of sodden material and uneatable foodstuffs.

'Nothing much here worth salvaging,' grumbled the wolf.

'It's all been ruined by the sea-water,' said the fox.

They moved slowly along the beach.

'Ah!' cried the wolf. 'Here is a barrel that looks all right to me.'

And there, indeed, in front of them was a strong, wooden keg, bound with iron bands.

'I hope it's not rum,' said the fox. 'Sailors like rum, but foxes do not. Oh dear, I hope it's not rum!'

The wolf sniffed at the keg. 'Don't worry,' he said, 'it's not. I think it's butter—fine, rich, creamy butter!' He smacked his lips, and the fox waved his bushy tail to and fro with pleasure and anticipation.

'Shall we open it up, and eat it now?' asked the fox.

'No, not now,' replied his friend. 'We've had one good meal today, let's save this until we really need it.'

The fox agreed, and together they scratched away at the sand until they had made a deep hole, into which they rolled the keg of butter. They covered it up, and on top they placed a few large stones to mark the spot. Then they went home.

The following day the fox dressed in his best clothes, and when the wolf asked him why he was arrayed in his finery, he replied, 'Well, Wolf, since you ask me, I must tell you that I have been invited to attend a baptism.'

And off he went—but not to any baptism. He made his way straight to the seashore and the hidden keg of butter. He prised off the lid, and tucked in. He ate so much and so greedily that the butter trickled from his mouth underneath his chin. Then he went home.

'And what was the child named at the baptism?' asked the wolf.

'Baptism? Baptism?' The fox was sleepy from too much food: for a moment, he had forgotten that he had said he was going to a baptism. 'Oh, yes, baptism! They called the child . . .' He put out his tongue to catch a tiny morsel of butter from his chin. 'They called him *Under the Mouth.*'

'What an odd name!' exclaimed the wolf.

The next morning, the fox again dressed in his best clothes, and told his partner that he had been invited to another baptism. And off again he went to the keg of butter. This time, he ate about half its contents before returning to the den.

'Well,' said the wolf, as he greeted the fox at the entrance, 'and what was this child named?'

The fox had no imagination, and could think of nothing but the butter he had eaten that day.

'A queer name to be sure,' he answered, 'and not one that I

should give to any child of mine. They called him *About Half and Half.*

On the third morning, the fox hastened to his third 'baptism'. He unearthed the barrel of butter, finished off its contents, and even licked the inside of the keg until it looked as clean as the day it was made. Then he went home.

The wolf asked the usual question. 'And what was the child named at the baptism?'

'Odder than ever,' said the deceitful fox. 'They called this one *Licking It All up.*'

The wolf by now was very suspicious, and, on the fourth day, he suggested to the fox that they should unearth the keg of butter they had hidden, and roll it home.

'Do we need it yet awhile, do you think?' asked the fox. 'Isn't it all right where it is?'

'No,' said the wolf. 'At the moment, it is buried where the sea does not reach it, but there are high tides tonight, and we do not want to lose our treasure.'

So they set off, the fox reluctantly and the wolf eagerly. Every now and again, the fox found some excuse for lingering behind.

'I don't feel very well,' he would say, ' so you go on without me', or 'I'm tired, I think I'll rest here, you go on without me.'

But the wolf urged him on, and, at last, they reached the beach and the hiding place of the keg of butter. The wolf dug it up, while the fox watched him.

'Ah!' exclaimed the wolf, when he had examined the empty keg. 'I thought as much. You've been visiting this keg of butter, haven't you? Confess it now.'

The fox indignantly denied the charge, and the wolf didn't press it. They loped home in silence. As soon as they reached their den, the wolf seized the fox who, taken unawares, was too surprised to struggle. He was slung upon the wall by his hind legs, with his head dangling below him. The fox had not fully digested all the butter he had eaten, and, in this upside-down position, a little lump of it began to trickle from his mouth on to his chin.

'Villain!' shouted the wolf. 'Red thief! Deceitful friend! Now deny that you visited the keg and ate up all the butter.'

The fox begged to be released from his uneasy position, and apologised for what he had done. His glib tongue and sorrowful manner moved the wolf to take him down from the wall, but, when they went to bed that night, relations between them were still somewhat strained.

The fox thought he should suggest something to take the wolf's mind off the incident of the butter, so, in the morning, he said, with mock humility, 'Friend—if I may still call you such—do you not think we have been wasting our time lately, and that we have been getting increasingly lazy? Let's go to the nearby town, buy a piece of ground there, and cultivate it together. Of course, although this is my idea, we would share the proceeds of the harvest.'

The wolf was bigger and stronger than the fox, but he was a simple, silly fellow, and quickly agreed to his companion's suggestion. Off they went to the town to see a landlord, who agreed to sell them a good strip of land for seven Saxon pounds. The two animals worked hard. When the ground was ready in the spring, they sowed oats, and, in the autumn, the harvest was a wonderful sight to see—a great green ocean of oats.

'I said we should share the proceeds of the harvest,' said the wily fox. 'And I am a man of my word, an honest man——'

FOX AND WOLF AND KEG OF BUTTER

'You weren't so honest about that keg of butter,' interrupted the wolf, who had a long memory.

'I think we can forget that little incident,' replied the fox grandly. 'I am talking now about this magnificent harvest which we see spread before us. Tell me, Wolf, which would you prefer, the root or the crop?'

'Give me the root,' said the wolf, without hesitation.

The fox smiled, as indeed he had good cause to do. All the year he was able to eat fine oaten bread made from the oat crop, while the wolf had to be content with the almost uneatable roots.

The next year the two animal farmers sowed potatoes on their land. When the time of the potato-lifting came, the fox said to the wolf, 'You shall have your choice of the harvest again. Which will you have, the root or the crop?'

The innocent wolf, remembering the mistake he had made the year before, quickly replied, 'Last year I said I'd have the root, but you'll not fool me so easily this year. I'll have the crop.'

Again, the fox smiled. The root of the oat may be next to useless, but, of course, it is the root, and not the crop of the potato that is eatable.

The wolf was furious when he discovered that he had made another mistake. He watched jealously while the fox piled up his stock of fine potatoes, and, as the months went by, he could not resist making occasional raids upon this supply. The fox regularly checked his stores, and soon discovered that some of his potatoes were missing.

'I'll soon put an end to this,' he said, and he called the wolf to his side.

'Do you know the white mare that grazes in the paddock near here?' he asked.

The wolf said that he did.

' Do you know what her name is ? '

The wolf said that he didn't.

' Do you know that her name is branded on her hooves ? '

' Well, well,' said the wolf, ' fancy that ! '

' It would be interesting to find out her name, wouldn't it ? ' asked the fox.

' One would only have to look on her hooves,' said the wolf.

' Quite,' agreed the fox. ' Suppose you go and do just that.'

The silly wolf trotted off, and, when he was searching the mare's hooves to discover her name, the horse kicked him so furiously that his head was severed from his body.

And never, from that day on, has the unlucky grey wolf bothered the cunning red fox.

The Last of the Giants 🖋

THERE is a cave in the Hills of Fearn in Ross, which was once the home of the Last of the Giants. When he was a young man, this giant was so tall that he strode among the trees and they were as grass at his feet; he was so broad that when he came between any man and the sun, darkness fell. His strength was greater than the armies of the world, his voice louder than the storm. His sight was so keen that he could identify a sparrow one hundred miles away, his hearing so acute that, were he on top of the tallest mountain, he could hear the waves lapping on the seashore. He could hold a ship in his hand, and his foot could cover a whole field. He was the greatest of all giants in an age of giants.

But when he grew older, his strength weakened; he shrivelled in size; his eyesight failed. The giants he had known in his youth had died, until only he was left—the Last of the Giants.

He had one daughter whom he loved dearly, and she cooked and cared for him in his old age. This daughter was married to a man of ordinary height, and this man did not have much respect for giants. He and his father-in-law were always arguing.

One day, they were seated round a table in the cave, eating their dinner.

'Very good beef, my dear,' said the giant to his daughter. He opened his huge mouth, and a sirloin of beef disappeared in a second.

'I don't suppose giants ever ate beef from an ox as large as this was,' said the son-in-law, who was very proud of the cattle he reared.

'You have a strange idea of giants,' grunted the last of them. 'Let me tell you that the legs of the birds we used to eat were heavier and meatier than the hindquarters of the biggest of your oxen.'

Hearing this, the son-in-law began to laugh.

'Impossible, quite impossible !' he cried, in between guffaws of laughter.

The giant's daughter joined in the laughter. 'Why, Father,' she giggled, 'what nonsense you do talk, to be sure !'

'We must forgive him his nonsense,' said her husband, 'and remember that he is very old and nearly blind.'

The giant let out a roar of anger. 'Don't treat me like a child,' he shouted. 'I'm telling you the truth, and will prove it to you.'

He called out loudly to his man-servant. The walls of the cave shook with the noise, although the sound was a whisper compared with the strength of his voice in his youth.

'Bring me my bow and three arrows,' he said, 'and lead me to the forest.'

When he and the servant had reached a certain spot in the forest, the giant stopped.

'My eyes are dim,' he said. 'Tell me, do you see a rock yonder ?'

'Aye, I do !' replied the servant.

'And are there rushes at the bottom of it ?'

'Aye, that there are,' replied the servant.

'And do you see a step in the face of the rock ?'

'I do,' said the servant.

'Then take me to that step,' demanded the giant.

The servant gently led his master to the step in the rock.

' Look now, and tell me what comes,' said the giant.

The servant scanned first the land, then the sky.

' I see birds,' he said, ' naught else but birds.'

' Are they larger than any birds you have seen before ? ' asked the giant.

' No, they are much the same size as they are at home,' replied the servant.

A few minutes went by before the giant asked again, ' What do you see now ? '

The servant scanned the sky.

' Birds, birds ! More and more birds ! '

' And are *they* larger than any birds you have seen before ? '

' Yes, yes ! ' cried out the servant fearfully. ' They are three times bigger than eagles.'

A few more minutes went by.

' Do you still see birds ? ' asked the giant.

' The air is black with them. I have never seen anything like it. The biggest of them is three times bigger than the biggest ox.'

' Guide my hand on the bow,' requested the giant.

The faithful servant placed his master's hand on the bow, fixed the arrow to the string and directed it towards the sky.

The giant released the bowstring, and the arrow zoomed strongly towards its target. A second later it fell to earth among the rushes at the foot of the rock, bringing with it the largest of the birds.

' Cut off a hindquarter,' said the giant.

When he had done so, the servant placed his master's hands to one side of the hindquarter, while he himself lifted the other side. They staggered home with their great burden.

There was just room for them to pass through the entrance of the cave, and when the son-in-law saw the size of the joint he was amazed.

'There you are !' cried out his father-in-law. 'Here is the hindquarter of a bird such as we giants are accustomed to eat.'

'I have never seen such a sight before,' admitted the young man. 'I am sorry that I ever doubted you.'

And from that day on, he treated the blind old giant with the respect and reverence due to the Last of the Great Ones.

The Tailor and the Devil ✌🏽

THE tailor was sitting cross-legged in his workshop, stitching at a fine brocade coat, when the Laird of Saddell called to see him.

'Good morning to you, Tailor,' called out the Laird. 'I see you are busy on that coat of mine.'

'It's a beautiful piece of cloth, my lord,' said the tailor, without looking up from his work. 'It's a pleasure to be stitching it.'

The Laird, having nothing better to do, leant against the doorpost, and watched the tailor.

'Had you heard that the graveyard near the abbey is haunted?' he asked, by way of conversation.

The tailor nodded his head.

'By the Devil, it is said,' added the Laird.

The tailor nodded his head again. He wished the Laird would go away and let him get on with his work in peace. Such a man for talk, this Laird!

'It'd be a brave man, I'm thinking, who would spend a night alone among the tombstones there,' went on the Laird.

The tailor grunted.

'Don't you think so, then?' asked the Laird.

'I wouldn't be knowing, sir,' said the tailor.

The Laird took out a bag of gold from his pocket and swung it to and fro in his hand.

' Tut, tut,' muttered the tailor

'I have a mind to place a bet,' he said. 'You sit there, stitching away so industriously, I bet you this bag of gold that you wouldn't sit so calmly all night in the graveyard, and have a pair of trousers stitched by dawn.'

The tailor said nothing, as he was biting a piece of thread at the time.

'What do you say, Tailor?' asked the Laird. 'Do you accept the challenge?'

The tailor looked up, and stared at the Laird.

'If you'll leave me, my lord, and let me get on with my work in peace, yes, I'll accept the challenge.'

He sounded calm enough but, in fact, the thought of the gold excited him. He was a poor man and usually worked hard for very little reward. It seemed an easy task to sit in a graveyard all night, and earn a bag of gold for one pair of trousers.

That night the wee tailor set off with enough material under his arm to make a pair of breeks, his pockets full of scissors, needle, thread and thimble. It was a dark, silent night, but this did not worry the tailor, a dark, silent man himself who, always being alone, did not fear loneliness. He reached the graveyard, and opened the creaking, iron gates which swung to behind him with a mighty clang. It was enough noise to wake the dead, but the tailor was not startled, and the dead went on sleeping.

He found a big, flat tombstone and sat himself, tailorwise, on it. Then he started work on the trousers. Soon he was stitching away busily in the light of the candle which he had lit at his side. He had been there some time when, suddenly, the earth rumbled and quaked.

' Tut, tut,' muttered the tailor, ' how can a man make neat stitches when the ground beneath him heaves like a stormy sea !'

A stone slab near by began to move, and an enormous head appeared out of a hole beneath it, a head covered with matted black hair and with eyes like fiery coals.

' Do you see this great head of mine ? ' roared a voice like the firing of a cannon.

' Aye, aye, I'm seeing it,' replied the tailor quietly. ' But, please, don't bother me. I'm very busy making a pair of trousers.'

An enormous pair of shoulders, like twin mountains, appeared below the head, and the huge voice roared again, ' Do you see these great shoulders of mine ? '

' Aye, aye, I see them,' said the tailor, scarcely looking up from his stitching.

Then a great leg and foot appeared and stamped on the slab with such violence that the whole graveyard shook and trembled.

' Do you see this great foot of mine ? ' asked the hideous monster.

' Aye, aye,' said the tailor quietly, ' but my trousers are finished, even if the stitches are ower long.'

He quickly snipped the thread, put the thimble in his pocket, tucked the trousers under his arm, leapt to his feet and took to his heels. The Devil—for such it was—chased after him. The tailor pulled open the iron gates, and slammed them in the face of his pursuer. The Devil hurdled right over them. The tailor raced down the glen towards the Castle of Saddell. The Devil gained on him with every step. By the time the tailor had reached the castle gate, he was faint with exhaustion, but he managed to close the gate behind him before the Devil caught up. Furious at losing his victim, the monster crashed his hand against one of the stone pillars supporting the gate, before finally disappearing.

When the tailor had recovered his breath, he asked to see the Laird. He was told that he was asleep.

' Never mind,' said the tailor, ' awaken him. I have a pair of trousers here for him.'

The Laird appeared, was presented with the trousers, and told of the curious happenings.

' I agree that you have made an excellent pair of trousers,' said the Laird, ' but how do I know that what you tell me is not the imagining of a man frightened by a night spent in a grave-yard ? '

The tailor took him to the castle gate, and, there on the stone pillar, was the imprint of the Devil's fingers and thumb—which, incidentally, may be seen there to this day.

' You are a brave man ! ' exclaimed the Laird, as he presented the smiling tailor with the promised bag of gold. ' I would not have endured what you have endured for twenty such bags of gold ! '

The Courage of Mairi 〜➧

MAIRI, daughter of a blacksmith of Kintyre, first met the handsome Eachunn at the wedding of her sister. She fell in love with him as soon as she set eyes on him, across the table, at the wedding-feast which was held in her father's barn. As the days went by, Eachunn came courting Mairi, but he came and went in secret, fearing the wrath of the old smith, who had often said that he would bring down curses on the head of any man who threatened to take away his one remaining daughter. Mairi met her lover in the spring near the banks where the primroses grow ; she met him in the summer in the fields where the mushrooms sprout, and she met him in the autumn in the lanes where the blackberries ripen.

'I am going primrosing,' she would tell her father, or, 'gathering mushrooms' or 'picking blackberries', as the case might be.

Time drifted on, and winter slowly crept across the country-side. It was now too cold for the lovers to meet out of doors, and Mairi had no excuse, anyway, to offer her father for long absences.

'I must be a coward no longer,' Eachunn told her. 'I will ask your father if I may have you for a wife. Is it not time you were sitting opposite me, by my own fireside ? '

'It must be as you say, my dear,' replied Mairi. 'But I fear my father is not going to like it. Come to see him tonight, and we will brave his wrath together.'

That night, Eachunn asked the smith for his daughter's hand in marriage. The old man was stunned at the request, and said nothing for so long that Mairi began to hope that he would consent without argument. She soon realised how false was this hope.

The smith suddenly rose to his feet and, shaking his fist in Eachunn's face, he shouted, ' Never, never ! Not if I can help it ! Mairi must stay here with me.'

Mairi started to sob with disappointment. ' Please, Father,' she pleaded, between tears, ' please let me marry Eachunn, for sure he has the heart of me.'

' I'll make her a good husband, sir,' said Eachunn quietly.

The smith refused to listen, and continued to rave at them, until Mairi told Eachunn that he should go and she would try to persuade her father to change his mind. When he had gone, Mairi told her father of Eachunn's many charms and virtues.

' Well,' said her father at last, ' I have thought better of it.'

Mairi stretched out her hands to him in gratitude, only to withdraw them quickly when she heard his next words.

' Eachunn may have you if, this very night, you will go across to the Abbey and bring back with you the skull that rests on the high altar. Thus you may prove how much your young man means to you.'

The colour drained from Mairi's face. She tilted her chin proudly, and her dark eyes flashed angrily.

' Very well, Father,' she said, ' if that's the only way I may get your permission, I'll go to the Abbey and bring back the skull.'

The Abbey to which the smith had referred was the old Abbey of Windswept Saddell of Monks, which was gradually sinking into decay and decline. Only a few old and feeble holy men were left there to keep alight a dim lamp on the high altar, where

94

rested the skull of the founder of their Abbey. There were many strange and eerie tales told about this skull, and the suggestion of carrying it away at the dead of night was enough to strike terror into the heart of the bravest clansman. Thus it was that the old smith never for a moment believed that his daughter would take up his challenge. In fact, even after she had said she would go, he did not take her seriously until he saw her wrap her plaid tightly around her, and hurry out into the night. And then it was too late to stop her.

The wind howled and whistled about Mairi, as if it would push her back and away from her destination, but up the hill she climbed, her head bent against the invisible force. And down the long valley she struggled, her feet so frozen with the cold, she scarcely knew how she moved them forward. She met no-one. It was very dark and, had she not known the way like the back of her hand, she would surely have been lost. She battled on and on ; once, when she fell to her knees in the snow, she had little will to get up and was tempted to lie there, close her eyes and drift into sleep.

' But I must get up,' she sobbed. ' I must—for Eachunn's sake.'

She clutched at the low-hanging branch of a tree and pulled herself up by it, and then trudged on. It seemed to her as if a million nights had passed since she had left her father's house, and a million miles been walked before she saw the black outline of the old Abbey, towering against the sky-line. The worst ordeal was ahead of her. As Mairi crept through the burial ground, the tombstones appeared to nod their stone heads at her, and she would not have been surprised to see the pale shapes of ghosts arise from every grave. She recalled with a shudder the tale that was told of the tailor of Saddell who was chased by the Devil.

The tall trees, surrounding the Abbey, screeched as an extra strong gust of wind tore through their branches. Mairi gasped with terror before she realised what had caused the noise.

' Silly girl that I am ! ' She laughed at herself. ' It was only the wind in the trees.'

A few seconds later she heard another strange noise, like the rushing of hundreds of tiny feet.

' Who's there ? ' she whispered hoarsely. There was no reply. Then the noise of tiny feet rushing past her came again.

' Can it be the lost souls of the dead ? ' wondered Mairi. She clung motionless to a stone pillar, too terrified to move and having neither the courage to go on to the Abbey door nor to turn and make for home. It was some minutes before she was able to move forward, as she reminded herself that her future happiness depended on her courage now. The old oak door of the Abbey groaned and creaked on its rusty hinges as she slowly pushed it open. Everything inside was dark and neglected, but, up near the high altar, Mairi could see a faint glimmer of light. She made her way up the aisle towards it. Dusty, broken, wooden pews lay on either side of her ; the rafters were thick with cobwebs above her head. A bat skimmed down, its leathery wings disturbing the air round Mairi's face. An owl hooted high on the sill of a window that had long since lost its purple and crimson glass. The lamp gleamed brighter as Mairi approached it. She shuddered as she became aware of the white object that lay in the pool of yellow light. The empty eye-sockets of the skull stared back at her, almost daring her to touch it. Mairi put out her hand stealthily, and, with a quick shudder, picked it up and wrapped it in the folds of her plaid. She turned and, weeping with fright, raced down the aisle as if the ghost of every monk who had ever prayed in the Abbey were at her heels. Still sobbing, she closed the oak door behind her, and almost fell out into the Abbey grounds. Again she was startled to hear the swift patter of tiny feet, and again her heart leapt with fear, but, the moon appearing momentarily from behind the clouds, the objects of her fear were clearly revealed. Mairi laughed aloud into the cold, crisp air—a herd of deer was moving swiftly through the trees ! The bitter weather had forced it to seek shelter near the protective walls of the old Abbey.

Mairi set off on the homeward journey, clutching the precious prize. Up hill and down dale she travelled, success giving wings to her feet, and love warmth to her heart. The great pearl of dawn matched the little wintry pearls of morning dew in Mairi's hair when she finally came in sight of her father's house. Her father stood at the window. He had not moved from the spot since she had left the night before, and had suffered long hours of remorse and anxiety. And, although he gazed eagerly out of the window towards the hills, in his heart he had never expected to see his beloved daughter alive again. When, therefore, he saw her open the garden gate and run lightly up the path, he thought for a moment that he was seeing a ghost.

Mairi ran into the room and, taking the skull from her plaid, she put it down on the table.

' There, Father ! ' she cried triumphantly. ' And now, may I marry Eachunn ? '

' Oh, my daughter, my daughter ! ' cried her father, taking her into his arms. ' Can you ever forgive a wicked old man for what he made you do ? Of course, you may marry Eachunn, and I shall give you such a wedding that folks round here will talk about it for years to come.'

And so it was. Mairi was wedded to the man for whom she had braved so much, and such a fine wedding it was, with the

97

bride so beautiful, the groom so handsome, with the food so rich and the wine so plentiful, that the folk in the glen have talked about it from that day to this !

Oh, yes !—perhaps it should be added that the skull was duly returned to its place in Saddell Abbey, and that it is doubtful if the old monks there ever knew that it had been removed at all.

Black Roderic ᔧᕿ

BLACK RODERIC was a Chief of the MacNeils of Barra, and famous for his swordsmanship. He claimed to be the finest swordsman in Scotland. But there was another man living in Scotland at that time who also made this claim, and his name was Rob Roy MacGregor. When it came to the ears of Black Roderic that there were those who believed that Rob Roy was more skilful with the sword than he was himself, he roared, ' I will challenge this MacGregor, then we shall see which of us is the greater fighter. Who can tell me where Rob Roy may be found ? '

One of his henchmen told him that Rob Roy was somewhere in the region of Loch Lomond. So, that very day, Black Roderic and his men set out on the long journey southwards from the Hebrides. When they arrived at Loch Lomond and made inquiries as to where they might meet with Rob Roy, they were told that he and his men had gone to a fair at Killearn.

' On to Killearn ! ' cried Black Roderic, digging his spurs impatiently into the side of his horse.

They had nearly reached Killearn when they met a band of men on horseback, who were laughing and singing, and looked as if they were returning from the fair.

Black Roderic reined in his horse.

' Good afternoon to you, gentlemen,' he said. ' Is it to the fair at Killearn that you have been ? '

' Aye,' replied one of the strangers. ' An excellent fair it was, too. We can heartily recommend it, can't we, gentlemen ? '

This was greeted with a chorus of agreement.

' And is there a man called Rob Roy MacGregor at this fair ? ' asked Black Roderic.

The stranger, the one who had already spoken, smiled. ' Indeed, there *was*,' he said.

' But he is not there now ? ' asked Black Roderic, snarling with disappointment.

The company of men laughed.

' No, he is not there now,' replied the stranger, still smiling. ' He is here, in front of you. I am Rob Roy MacGregor. What may I do for you ? '

' I am the Chief of Barra,' growled Black Roderic. ' They are telling me that you fancy yourself a better swordsman than I am, so I have come to prove that you are not ! '

' But I have no quarrel with you,' said Rob Roy.

' Quarrel or not, I am challenging you to fight,' said Black Roderic, dismounting from his horse.

' I have little desire to fight any man without due cause,' said Rob Roy, dismounting too. · ' But I accept your challenge, and you are likely to rue the day you made it.'

On one occasion only had Rob Roy been known to refuse a challenge, and that was when one Donald Bain had challenged him. Rob Roy refused to fight him, saying he fought duels only with gentlemen.

A space was cleared for the combatants, and, watched by their men, the two swordsmen began to fight. Now, Rob Roy was famous for the length of his arms : when he stood erect, his finger-tips touched his garters. Because of the length and strength of his arms, he wielded his claymore, or huge sword, to great effect. It was almost impossible for a normal man to get near Rob Roy's body so much as to prick him. Out lunged the huge arm, the claymore thrusting and parrying. It took less than a few seconds for Black Roderic to realise he was outclassed, and that it would have been wiser for him to have stayed at home in the Hebrides. Rob Roy put both hands to the hilt of his claymore and brought it down forcefully on to Black Roderic's sword arm, nearly severing it from his shoulder.

'Enough!' gasped the Chief of Barra. 'Hold, enough!'

Rob Roy sheathed his sword, and motioned to Black Roderic's men to help their Chief on to his horse.

'Perhaps that will teach you not to pick quarrels with those who have no wish to harm you,' Rob Roy told his challenger. And he and his men went on their way.

Black Roderic and his men were unable to go very far on their way, as the Chief was forced to stay many months in the village of Killearn until his wounds had healed. And never again was he troubling Rob Roy.

However, he was a man who was always wanting to annoy someone, and, once he was back in his own islands, he began to think of some other warrior he could provoke to fight with him.

'We will go on an expedition to Shetland,' he told his men, 'and demand tribute from the Warrior of that island.'

An eight-oared galley was prepared, fully manned and, with Black Roderic at the helm, set sail for the Shetlands.

The mightiest and bravest warrior among Black Roderic's men-at-arms was a widow's son, and, because he was mighty and brave, the Chief was jealous of him. He could not bear to think that any man in his service might be stronger than he was himself. And he laid a wicked plan to get rid of the young man.

The galley landed at Shetland without difficulty or opposition. The Warrior of Shetland came down to the shore to greet the Chief of the MacNeils.

' Do you come in peace ? ' he asked.

' No ! ' roared Black Roderic. ' We come for tribute—money, food, animals ; all these we demand from you.'

' No tribute,' shouted the Warrior, ' until you defeat me in combat. Do you accept a challenge ? '

Black Roderic said he would. But, before the duel began, he turned to the widow's son.

' When you see me take a step back in the fight,' he said, ' you will know I am growing weak. When you see me look back once, the fight will be going against me. When I look back a second time, you will realise that I am exhausted. Then I shall expect you to step into my place. If you finish the fight successfully, we shall divide the spoil of Shetland. Do you understand ? '

The widow's son nodded.

The Chief and the Warrior commenced battle. They fought up and down the seashore, the air was loud with their battle cries and the clanging of their claymores. Black Roderic weakened, and took a step back, which did not go unheeded by the widow's son. The Warrior of Shetland fought with renewed vigour, and Black Roderic looked over his shoulder at the widow's son. The Warrior of Shetland forced his opponent towards the rocks ; Black Roderic glanced over his shoulder for a second time, and the widow's stepped into the breach. Now, Black Roderic had every hope that the young man would be killed by the Warrior and that then, refreshed by a rest, he himself could recommence battle. Thus, he might vanquish two enemies at the same time. But the widow's son was a great fighter, and soon it was apparent that the Warrior was giving way before him.

BLACK RODERIC

Black Roderic, impatient for the Warrior's death, decided he
could deal with the widow's son later and called out to him :
  'Kill the Warrior ! Kill him ! Give him the end he deserves !'
  And the next moment, the severed head of the Warrior of
Shetland lay on the beach. The widow's son was aghast at what
he had done in the heat of battle. It had been fair combat, and he
had intended only to wound his noble opponent. He turned on
his Chief.
  'Oh, wicked MacNeil !' he cried. 'See what you have made
me do. It is you who are to blame for the death of this innocent
man. Get out of here, you and your crew, or I shall kill every
one of you. I am now Laird of Shetland, and not a penny shall
you take from this island, nor a blade of grass, nor the smallest
animal.'
  Black Roderic hesitated, and turned to his men for help.
They cowered in the background. One thing he could do, and
he did it—beat a hasty retreat to the galley. And that was the last
they saw of him or his men in Shetland.

The Three Banshees ❧

THERE once lived in western Skye a shepherd by name of Norman MacSweyn. One day, when he was out on the great stretches of moorland, tending his sheep, a kindly neighbour called to see his wife.

'Why, Mistress MacSweyn,' she said, when the door was opened to her, 'upon my word, you do look tired.'

'I have done a hard day's work, neighbour,' replied the shepherd's wife, 'cleaning, washing, baking bread. And the baby is ailing, she has cried all day.' She wiped a weary hand across her brow.

'Well, get you to yon bed and rest awhile,' said her friend. 'I'll stay and look after the bairn.'

The shepherd's wife gladly accepted the kind offer, went to her bed, lay down on it and closed her eyes. The neighbour took up the whimpering babe from its cot, sat down by the fire and began crooning softly to the child. Soon the baby ceased crying, and the warmth from the fire and the quiet in the room sent the good neighbour to sleep. But the mother, although dozing happily, was not asleep, and, on opening her eyes for a second, she was surprised to see three funny little women grouped around her sleeping friend and the baby. They were shadowy, grey, ugly little women and, although they were standing in front of the fire, she was able to see the flames through them. They had made no noise when they entered the house, and were making

Shadowy, grey, ugly little women

none now. Mistress MacSweyn was frightened. Could these be
banshees—the fairies of death? She had often heard of them, but
never seen any before. She stayed motionless on the bed. The
little women were whispering. She strained to hear what they
were saying.

'Take up the babe, and we'll away with it,' said the eldest of
the little women, who was standing nearest the bed.

The second banshee spoke, and her voice was like a thin, high
note played on an old fiddle. 'Is it not a shame, Sister, to rob the
poor woman MacSweyn of this one babe when you have already
had so many of her children?'

The shepherd and his wife had lost many babies through
sickness.

'Yes, indeed,' agreed the third banshee. 'Have pity on the
wretched woman.'

'When have we ever had pity on anyone?' cried out the
senior banshee. 'Pity is a word we do not know.'

Still her sisters pleaded with her to spare the child, until at last she agreed.

'Well, we'll not take the child away,' she said, 'but this I declare: when that little piece of peat that is burning in the hearth shall be burned out, the child will surely die.'

The banshees crept out of the house, moving like a cloud of mist away across the moors to no-one knows where.

The neighbour was still asleep, but, as soon as the banshees had gone, the mother leapt up from her bed, seized a large jug of water that was standing on a table near by, and poured it over the fire. There was a spluttering and a hissing as the fire went out. She snatched from the hearth the sodden piece of peat to which the banshee had referred, and, wrapping it carefully in a cloth, she hid it in a small wooden chest she kept under the bed. That done, she lay down again on the bed, happy in the thought that she had saved the life of her little daughter, who was already beginning to stir on the neighbour's lap.

The years passed swiftly as the flight of a bird. The little girl—whose name was Oighrig—grew into a lovely young woman. And, as was to be expected, she met a young man with whom she fell in love, and they became engaged to be married. In those days, in the Isles, the bride-to-be did not attend church from the day she was betrothed until the day she was married. So it happened that one Sunday morning, Norman MacSweyn and his wife set out early on the twelve-mile walk to church, leaving Oighrig behind in the house. She busied herself, preparing the dinner for her parents when they should return. The meat was in the oven and the vegetables simmering in the cooking pots, so she looked around for something else with which to occupy her time. But her mother had left the house clean and tidy, and there was nothing else to do. She sat down by the fire,

106

awaiting her parents' return. She was restless and bored. It was
a dismal day, the wind blowing and the rain heavy. If there was
nothing to do in the house, it was impossible to do anything
outside. Oighrig sighed.

'Oh dear, I wish I had something to do,' she murmured. 'It
will be hours before Mother and Father get back. And everyone's in church, except me, so there aren't likely to be callers.'

At that moment, her eyes rested on the little wooden chest
that her mother always kept under the bed. It was a strange
thing about that chest : she had never been allowed to touch it,
let alone play with it or look inside it. The only time—many
years ago—that she had dared to put her hand on the lid, her
mother had smacked and scolded her. The memory was still
very clear. What was so precious about the box, she wondered ?
What did it contain that her mother should guard it so carefully ?
Oighrig suspected that even her father did not know the answer.
She was tempted. She glanced out of the window, but there was
no sign of her parents. Now was her chance to find out the
secret of the chest which had puzzled her off and on all her life.
She knew she was doing wrong, and that her mother would be
angry if she found out. Nevertheless, she stealthily pulled out the
chest and lifted the lid. As far as she could judge, the chest was
full of odds and ends, none of them very valuable. Oighrig sat
cross-legged on the floor, and took out the things, one by one.
There were a few pieces of cheap jewellery, of a kind her mother
might have won at a fair at some time ; and there were one or
two fine lawn handkerchiefs, edged with lace, and a white slipper
(that her mother had worn at her wedding perhaps) ; there was
a jar of ointment, a broken hammer, some reels of coloured
thread, some odd scraps of material. The chest contained nothing
of value, nor did it contain, as far as Oighrig could see, anything

107

that could possibly harm her. It did, however, contain one rather surprising item. At the bottom, she found a piece of cloth wrapped round, of all things, a bit of peat. Her mother must be mad to keep such a silly thing. She supposed it had got there by mistake. She put back the other articles tidily, but the peat she threw carelessly on the fire, knowing no other good use to which it might be put.

The peat smouldered ; poor Oighrig began to feel ill. By the time her folks had returned from church, she was too weak to get up to greet them.

' Why, Oighrig, my daughter,' cried her father, ' what ails you ? '

The mother saw the chest, pulled out from under the bed : Oighrig had not had the strength to replace it.

' Oighrig ! ' cried out the wretched woman, ' have you touched anything in this chest ? Anything at all ? '

' I looked at the contents ; I'm sorry, Mother,' replied the girl.

' Did you put back everything ? ' asked Mistress MacSweyn, rummaging wildly through the chest.

' All but the piece of peat, which I put on the fire ; everything, Mother dear, but the peat. I did not think you would want the peat.'

The mother let out a cry of despair and, as the peat the banshee had cursed gave a last little flicker, so life left the body of Oighrig MacSweyn.

Sir Michael Scott ✌️➤

SIR MICHAEL SCOTT of Balwearie was the greatest warlock—or wizard—that Scotland has ever known. It was said that many of his faithful servants were demons of the underworld, and that one of them had been given him by the Devil in exchange for the wizard's shadow. No shadow fell where Sir Michael walked after that. Even the black horse he rode had magical properties. On one occasion, Sir Michael was sent to the Court of France by King Alexander III of Scotland to ask for certain concessions, which the King of France refused to grant.

'I would advise your Majesty to reconsider the matter,' warned Sir Michael.

The King of France knew nothing of Sir Michael Scott's great reputation, and was not alarmed by the threatening note in his voice. He shook his head.

'I shall give you but a few minutes to think again—until my black horse outside shall have stamped three times,' said Sir Michael.

The King and his courtiers laughed at this upstart from across the water, but their laughter was drowned by the resounding clang of the black horse's hoof as it struck the cobblestones outside. Instantly, all the bells in France were set a-ringing. The big bells boomed, the little ones tinkled. The people in their beds were roused from sleep, the faithful at their prayers lifted their heads in amazement, and the birds in the trees were startled from their nests. Conversation all over the country ceased : it was impossible to hear anything while the bells rang and rang. They stopped ringing only when the coal-black steed stamped for a second time. The second stamp brought down the highest towers of the palace. The French King did not wait to see what would be the effect of the third stamp.

' Stop ! ' he cried. ' I have reconsidered. Tell your master it shall be as he asks.'

Sir Michael bowed low, hiding the triumphant smile that lingered on his lips. King Alexander had cause to be particularly grateful for the unusual services of this ambassador.

It was never wise to cross Sir Michael Scott : he had unpleasant forms of punishment for those who displeased him, as one farmer's wife once discovered to her cost. Sir Michael was out hunting when, feeling hungry, and spying a house not far off, he sent his servant to ask for a piece of bread.

The servant knocked at the door and asked the good woman who opened it for a sup of bread for his master.

' I have no bread in the house,' she replied curtly.

The servant sniffed. He could distinctly smell the warm dough, and he could glimpse the blazing fire and the baking girdle. He returned to Sir Michael.

' The woman of the house says she has no bread,' he reported. ' But she is lying, sir. I could smell fresh bread as soon as she opened the door to me.'

Sir Michael was enraged at this news and, taking from his pocket a whelk—or devil's buckle as it is called in those parts—he told his servant to return to the house and place it unobserved above the lintel of the door. No sooner had this been done than the charm began to work.

SIR MICHAEL SCOTT

The farmer's wife was bending over the oven, removing the final batch of loaves, when she was seized with a strange desire to dance. She danced around the kitchen, feet tapping and arms whirling, chanting :

> ' Sir Michael Scott's man
> Came seeking bread and gat nane.'

Meanwhile, the farmer, who was working in the fields, wondered why his wife was so late sending down dinner to him and his men. They were harvesting ; it was very hot, and they had been working hard and were very hungry. The young daughter of one of the farm workers had brought her father a jug of beer, and the farmer asked her to call at the farmhouse on her way home, and remind his wife about the harvesters' dinner.

The girl knocked on the farmhouse door. No-one answered, but she could hear a great deal of noise going on inside. The farmer's wife appeared to be in high spirits and was singing at the top of her voice.

' Mistress,' she called, ' the master wants to know if you have forgotten the dinner, and asks me to tell you to hurry with it.'

The noise and singing continued, but the girl received no reply, so she opened the door and went into the kitchen. As soon as she crossed the threshold she, too, was seized with a desire to dance, and she joined the farmer's wife in a wild Highland fling.

An hour went by, and as the girl had not returned with any message and still his wife had not brought the dinner, the farmer decided to look into the matter. He reached his homestead but, before entering the kitchen, looked through the window. He saw his wife and the girl capering around the kitchen like a couple of mad things.

'Stop this nonsense!' he shouted. 'What about my dinner, woman? This is no time for such jollity.'

He angrily threw open the door, and strode into the kitchen. Before he knew what he was doing, he had whisked off to join the ladies, his feet tapping in rhythm with theirs. The dance that had started as a solo performance had now become an uproarious threesome reel. And the inhospitable wife, her voice weak with exhaustion, continued to chant:

> ' Sir Michael Scott's man
> Came seeking bread and gat nane.'

Sir Michael had spent the day hunting, but when dusk fell, his servant asked, ' What of the dancing woman, sir? '

' What of the dancing trio, you mean,' said Sir Michael, who had his own ways of knowing what had been happening in the farmhouse. ' Yes, well, it has been punishment enough. Do you return and remove the charm from the door-head.'

This the servant did and, the whelk removed, the dancers dropped with weariness upon the hearth and slept, some say, for a week and three days.

Willie and the Pig 🐖

A YOUNG minister in Dunfermline was given a small pig by one of his parishioners to whom he had done a kindness. At first, he was delighted with the gift but, as time went on and the pig grew bigger, he found the cost of feeding it too expensive, so he decided to send it to Cairneyhill where he had a friend who would feed and board it free of cost. Now, the minister had a servant called Willie who, although a good enough chap, was rather simple.

'Put this pig in a sack, Willie,' directed the minister, 'and take it to Cairneyhill where my friend is expecting it.'

After a struggle in which the pig nearly got the better of him, Willie managed to get the animal into the sack. Then he made ready to set out on the journey.

The master knew his servant was easily led astray and that, having little sense, the easiest task was sometimes difficult for him.

'Tell no-one where you are going, Willie,' he said, 'nor what your errand is. Just keep Cairneyhill in mind, deliver the pig, and return here immediately.'

'You know me, master,' replied Willie. 'I'll do as you say.'

'Aye, aye, I know you only too well,' smiled the minister ruefully.

Willie trudged off with the precious burden on his back. When he was half-way to Cairneyhill, he met three of his friends outside a public house.

' Hello, Willie,' greeted the first friend.

' Where are you going on this fine day, Willie ? ' asked the second.

' What's that you carry on your back, Willie ? ' asked the third.

Willie was flustered at this meeting.

' H-hallo, friends,' he stuttered. ' I c-can't tell you what my errand is. Master said tell no-one, that's what he said. But this I can say, it's neither a cat nor a dog I have in my sack.'

His friends laughed, and assured him they would ask no more questions. One of them clapped him on the back, and said, ' Come inside, and have a drink with us ; you must be tired with walking so far, and carrying a heavy burden too.'

' No, no,' said Willie, casting a longing eye towards the cool interior of the pub, ' the minister would never trust me wi' a pig again if I did that ! '

The friends smiled knowingly at each other, but pretended they had heard no mention of a pig.

' Come on, Willie,' said another, ' just one little drink won't hurt. Leave your sack at the door for a minute or two.'

Willie needed no more persuasion. He put down the sack, and walked into the pub. In a twinkling, one of the lads snatched the pig out of the sack, and put in its place a young dog.

Free from any suspicion, the honest servant had his drink, took up his sack and went cheerily on his way. When he reached Cairneyhill, he delivered greetings to his master's friend, and handed over the sack.

' Thank you, Willie,' said the minister's friend. ' Will you undo the sack for me, and then you can help me put the pig in the sty ? '

Willie opened the sack and, instead of the pig with its long pink snout and cloven feet, out jumped a small black dog.

'Help, help!' cried out poor Willie. 'The Devil has been busy since I left the manse this morning.'

The minister's friend was bewildered, but he didn't believe the Devil had been up to any tricks. Knowing Willie, he suspected a more human trick had been played on him.

'Calm down, Willie,' he said, 'and take back this dog to your master.'

'It's not a dog, sir,' replied Willie, trembling with fright. 'It's a pig, sir, as sure's death, but Satan has changed him from white to black!'

He put back the dog into the bag, and set out on his return journey. When he reached the door of the inn, he saw the same three friends, looking as quiet and as innocent as they had done earlier in the day.

'What, Willie,' said one of them, 'have you still got that sack on your back?'

'Aye, a terrible thing happened,' said Willie. 'The Devil turned the pig into a dog, and now I must awa' home with the puppy. I'm still shaking wi' the fright of it all.'

'Did you ever hear the like!' exclaimed the second friend, trying to hide his smiles.

'Another drink is what you need, my lad,' said the third, 'after a fright like that.'

This time, Willie needed no persuasion; a drink was exactly what he needed. He felt he deserved it, too, after all he had been through. He put down the sack and went inside. As soon as he had done so, one of the jokers removed the dog and replaced it with the pig.

An hour or so later, the unsuspecting Willie hurried along

towards the manse, his fuddled brain full of all sorts of strange thoughts. He poured out the story of the day's disaster to the minister, who could scarce make head nor tail of it.

'And your friend at Cairneyhill, master,' concluded Willie, 'told me to bring back the dog to you immediately.'

'I don't know what you're talking about,' said the minister, 'but untie the sack, and put the pig back into the sty. You'll have to take it again to Cairneyhill tomorrow.'

'It's no' a pig, sir,' cried Willie. 'It's a black pup dog, as sure's death. I'll let you see for yourself.'

He opened the sack : with a grunt and a squeal, the pig jumped out. Willie screamed in terror.

'It's no' a dog, sir, it's a pig as sure's death.'

Willie was convinced that the Devil had been up to his tricks again. The minister was more convinced than ever that his servant was a complete fool !

The Stranger and the Miller ❧

THERE was once a miller who lived in a place called Ballomill. He was an hospitable man, who always welcomed travellers into his house that they might rest a while after their journeying. He remembered few of the faces or names of these strangers, so many of them came and went. But one such stranger he was to remember all his life, and the tale of his coming and of what happened afterwards was handed down to his children and their children for many generations.

One evening, at twilight, there was a knock on the miller's door, and when he opened it, the miller saw there a travelling man. On his face were deep lines of tiredness, and his clothes were dusty and stained.

'Good evening,' said the stranger, bowing courteously, 'I wonder if I may beg something to eat, and perhaps a bed for the night. I have travelled far, and lost my way.'

'Come in, come in,' urged the miller. 'I never refuse a man in need. Of course you must eat and sleep with us, and to-morrow, when it is light, I'll put you on your way.'

The stranger thanked him, and entered the miller's humble home, where he was introduced to the good wife of the house.

'Kill a hen, my dear,' said the miller. 'Our visitor has travelled far, and is hungry. We must see that he is well fed tonight.'

His wife took him to one side. 'That's all very well, my

dear,' she said, ' but it is the last hen we have. What shall we do when she is gone ? There is bread and cheese, is that not enough for a stranger ? '

' Whisht, woman,' replied the miller, ' never let it be said that my house did not give of its best to those who ask for food and lodging. Go and prepare the meal, and see that nothing is spared.'

When the dinner was put on the table, it was obvious that the miller's wife had spared neither herself nor the larder. It was a magnificent meal.

' Come, sir,' said the miller, ' let us eat, and I hope you will do justice to the meal. Will you please sit there at the head of the table ? '

' I am but a stranger in your house,' was the reply, ' and do not think I deserve this honour.'

' Sit up at the top of the table, sir,' said the miller firmly, ' for I will have strangers honoured.'

The stranger did as he was requested, without further argument. And after they had eaten, he and the miller sat by the fire and had an hour or two's lively conversation before going to bed.

The next morning, the miller was up early that he might get his work done in the mill before seeing the stranger on his way.

' You'll get no reward for putting yourself out for this stranger,' grumbled his wife. ' He eats your food, sleeps in our bed—oh, yes, I know you didn't tell him we had to spend the night down here on the floor !—and now you wear yourself out that you may have the time to ride a few miles with him.'

' I want no reward,' replied the miller mildly. ' It is but charitable to behave so. One day I may be glad that someone should do for me what I have done for this stranger.'

The stranger appeared to know the way well enough when he

118

and the miller rode off through the woods, although he had said
he was lost the night before.

' My men will be waiting for me,' he said briefly.

The miller raised his eyebrows. He hadn't imagined the
traveller to be a man with followers or servants. And he certainly
hadn't thought to see the sight which met his eyes when they rode
out of the woods. There was a huge field in front of them, full
of soldiers and their officers, servants and their lords. There must
have been a thousand men there, and there were scores of horses,
and arrays of brightly coloured tents.

The stranger rode confidently into the field, his companion a
short way behind him. The miller noticed for the first time that
this man had a certain proud dignity, but, for all that, he was
astounded to see every man bow low as he passed among them.
A high-ranking officer in resplendent uniform came forward to
help the stranger dismount.

' So you have returned to us safely, your Majesty,' he said.

The miller nearly fell from his horse with astonishment and
fright. His Majesty ! This man, with whom he had spent many
hours, with whom he had been so free, was none other than
King James V, also known as the Gudeman of Ballengeigh !
Why, execution could be ordered for a miller who had behaved
so familiarly towards his king ! He dismounted clumsily from
his ancient nag, and knelt down on the grass.

' Forgive me, your Majesty, I didn't know . . .'

The King laughed. ' I didn't mean that you should, good
miller. I delight in such excursions where I am not recognised :
it helps me to get to know my people. And now, we are on our
way to my palace at Falkland ; you shall accompany us that I
may return hospitality to you.'

The miller was embarrassed, and began to say that he was too humble a man to stay at a palace, but King James refused to listen and, a messenger having been sent to the miller's wife to tell her the astonishing news, the King, the miller and the company of soldiers and courtiers went on their way.

There was a great feast at the palace that night. When the miller was led into the banqueting hall, he was overawed by the vastness of the room, the quantities of rich food with which the tables were laden, the magnificence of the silver and glass. He tried to slip quietly into a place at the bottom of a table where no-one would notice him but, as he was sitting down, the King called out to him from the top table :

' Miller, I wish you to sit at the head of my table.'

' No, no, thank you kindly, your Majesty, I do very well where I am,' replied the miller.

The King came up to him and, slapping him gently on the side of his head, paid back the miller in his own words.

' Sit up,' he said, ' for I will have strangers honoured.'

The miller smiled, and obeyed.

He stayed at the palace, feasting and joining in such games as putting the shot and tossing the caber, at which, being a strong athletic man, he outdid all the courtiers. As time went on, in spite of the fine food he was getting at the King's table, the miller began to look pale and to feel unwell.

' The food is over-rich for me, I fear,' he told the King, ' and I wonder if I may have your Majesty's permission to return home.'

' What do you usually eat and drink ? ' asked the King.

' Meal and broken water,' replied the miller. (Broken water was water that had fallen on the mill wheel.)

The King gave him permission to leave but, before he departed, the miller was told that some of the land at Ballomill was to be given to him as a reward for the hospitality he had shown the King.

' Will you have the aught part or the twa part of the lands of Ballomill ? ' asked the King.

The miller was not good at arithmetic, and as the ' aught part ' sounded higher, he chose that. Accordingly, he was given the eighth part instead of the half ! However, he was well satisfied. The land was made over to him in a Crown charter, and even an eighth part of the lands of Ballomill was rich return for one night's lodging provided for a stranger.

King James and the Questions ❧

THERE is another tale told of this same King James when he was staying once again at his palace in Falkland. It seems that he had heard of a minister in Markinch who was a rather dull scholar, and the King wondered if such a man were suitable to have charge of a parish. So he called on this minister.

'I have four questions which I should like to put to you,' he said. 'I will give you until this time tomorrow in which to answer them. The first question is, where is the middle of the earth? The second is, how long will I take in going round the earth? Third is, how much am I worth? And the fourth is, what is my thought? If you cannot answer, you will lose your living.'

The minister trembled when he heard the questions. He could not answer one of them, and he was sure that, however hard he thought about them, he still would not know the answers by the time the King returned next day.

Now, there lived a clever, witty miller (not the same who had sheltered the King on a previous occasion) a little to the south of the parish, and he happened to look very like the minister of Markinch. It came to his ears that the minister was greatly distressed and, being fond of the kind but foolish man, he went to him with an offer of help.

'Listen to me, reverend,' he said, 'if you will lend me a suit of your dark clothes, I am willing to meet the King instead of you, and I will try to answer his questions for you.'

The minister was delighted with the idea, and expressed his gratitude.

'If you manage to answer the questions satisfactorily,' he said, 'will you do one thing more for me? Will you beg his Majesty to allow me to stay as minister of this parish? I am happy here, and do not know what I should do if I had to leave.'

The miller promised to do what he could.

The next day, at the appointed time, the miller, dressed in the minister's clothes, stood outside the minister's house, ready to receive the King. When his Majesty arrived, it did not occur to him for a moment that he was not addressing the minister. Without more ado, he asked the first question.

'Where is the middle of the earth?'

The miller was holding a staff in his hand, and he put out this before him.

'It is just there,' he said. 'And if your Majesty will measure all around, you will find it to be just where the point of my stick is.'

The King knew it would be impossible for him to measure from that point to all corners of the earth, so decided to take his word for it. He thought the answer clever, and accordingly passed it.

'Excellent, excellent!' he exclaimed. 'Now, how about the second question? How long will I take in going round the world?'

'If you will rise with the sun,' said the miller, 'and go round with him all day, you will take exactly twenty-four hours.'

The King was equally pleased with this answer.

'Very clever, very clever!' he exclaimed. 'Now, question number three, how much am I worth?'

123

' I think you should be worth just about twenty-nine pieces of silver,' said the miller.

The King frowned. The miller went on : ' Our Saviour was valued at only thirty pieces of silver, and I think you should certainly be valued at a piece less than He was. Don't you agree ? '

The King nodded, certainly this was so.

' You have done very well so far,' he said. ' But the last question is the most difficult. Can you tell me what my thought is ? '

The miller laughed. ' You are thinking that I am the minister of Markinch,' he said, ' but I am the miller of the Middle Mill ! '

The King was delighted with both the answer and the man, and did not mind that he had been tricked into believing the miller was the minister.

' Well, in that case,' he said, ' I think the minister shall be turned out of the parish, and you shall have his place.'

' If it please your Majesty,' said the miller, ' I should prefer to stay a miller, and I should be grateful if you will let the minister stay at his job. He may not be a wise man, but he is a good and a kind one, and we in this parish love him dearly.'

King James was moved by the miller's words and, being a reasonable man, he agreed to the request.

David Wright and the Fairies 🌙

DAVID WRIGHT was a man who not only believed in the fairies, but also cared about them. They, in turn, were of great help to him once in every year. He rented a farm called Craiginnin, and when summer came, and time for the grass in the meadow to be cut, the farm labourers were given orders to cut the grass but to leave it in the field for the fairies to do the rest of the hay-making. The fairies came from Blackford, Gleneagles and Buckieburn, and assembled on the top of a hill called Saddlehill before descending to Farmer Wright's fields. It was as if a swarm of bees had gathered on the hill-top. Many of these fairies had not met since the year before, and there was always a great exchange of news. Then they were off like a cloud to the valley below. They worked hard from morning to evening, never stopping to eat and seldom stopping to talk. They spread out the grass evenly in the sun and, when it was quite dry, they put it into small heaps, and then into ricks. Towards the end of the day, they carried the ricks into the farm-yard—a heavy job for such small people—where they built them into stacks.

David Wright never forgot to reward the fairies for their yearly kindness to him. When the time for the sheep-shearing came round, he gave orders for a few of the best fleeces of his flock to be left on the ground. He never saw the fairies collect them, but, by the next morning, the fleeces were always gone. The farm prospered for many years. David Wright grew into an old man. He knew he had not long to live, so he called his eldest son to him.

' Son, do you know the secret of the success of this farm ? ' he asked.

' You work hard, and it's good land, Father,' replied the son.

' Many of my neighbours work hard, some of them have better land, but they are not as successful as I.'

' What is the answer then, Father ? ' The son smiled.

' Letting the fairies do the hay-making ; rewarding them with a few of the finest fleeces at sheep-shearing time. Always be in friendship with our fairy neighbours, and Craiginnin farm will always prosper.'

The son secretly thought his father a silly old man to believe the fairies had anything to do with the prosperity of the farm, but, to humour him, he agreed that when the time came for him to take over the farm, he would carry on the tradition.

David Wright died, and was duly succeeded by his son. Young Wright turned out a hard, inhospitable, mean man. And the good advice of his father was immediately forgotten. Hay-making time came round and, thinking thereby to save fleeces later on, he gave instructions to the labourers to do all the work.

' The old master used to tell us only to cut the grass,' argued one old man.

' I am master now,' said Wright, ' so you must do as I tell you.'

When the fairies gathered on Saddlehill that year, they soon realised that the men were working on in their fields. The men took longer over the hay-making than the fairies used to do, and although the work went fairly well, it was not finished by the evening. And, next morning, when they returned to the fields, they found the hay scattered in every direction. Morning after morning this continued, until at last the hay was ruined and unfit for use.

'It is the fairies ; no good comes of crossing the fairies,' grumbled the old man who had argued earlier with young Wright.

'Destroy their rings, plough up the green hillocks where they live,' shouted young Wright angrily. 'I'll show them I'm not afraid of them. Fairies indeed ! '

The ruined hay was but the beginning of the misfortunes of Craiginnin Farm. One day the dairymaid, when she had finished churning, carried the butter, as she always did, to the 'butter well' on the east side of the house, where she was in the habit of washing it before sending it to the market. She placed the butter in the cold, crystal water and was about to take it out when she saw a small hand appear from the well. The hand quickly laid hold of the bright yellow pat of butter, and disappeared with it beneath the water. The dairymaid tried to snatch it back, but wasn't quick enough. As she turned away, she heard a thin voice singing :

> ' Your butter's awa'
> To feast our band
> In the fairy ha'.'

And every time the dairymaid went to the well after that, she had the butter stolen from her in the same way.

The horses, cows, sheep and poultry began to sicken and die. In a few months the farm, which had once been the envy of all the farmers in the district, was unproductive and poverty-stricken. The fairies' revenge on their unfriendly farmer was complete.

The Good Crawford ❧

IN Clackmannanshire there is a beautiful spot called Gowan Dell, but if we are to believe a story that is told about it, this place was not always as lovely as it is now.

Many, many years ago there was a terrible drought in that part of the country. The bonnie green fields and hills turned as brown as the bracken in autumn, and the water in the clear streams slowed to a muddy trickle and sang no longer over the rocks nor bubbled in the pools nor gushed in the wells. Everything everywhere was withered and dry. Many sheep and cows died from lack of water, and the farmers who farmed in a small way were desperate from lack of money. The fairy rings and hillocks were not affected by the heat and lack of rain, and remained fresh and green as ever, and the fairies did what they could to relieve the distress of the poor people in the district.

There was a man by the name of Crawford who, like old man David Wright, had always been kind to the fairies and careful not to annoy them in any way. But Crawford was not only good to the fairies, he was good to his fellow creatures too. He could not bear to see them suffer or starve, and while he had a penny to give, he gave freely. He was not a wealthy farmer, he had but three cows, and when the drought came, it was not long before these three cows died. Crawford depended on the animals to support his wife and family, and the night after the cows collapsed, he sat brooding by the fire, wondering how he and those he loved were going to stay alive. There was a sudden disturbance in the chimney. Some soot fell on the flames, and immediately afterwards a large purse. Crawford pulled this out of the hearth before it caught fire. He lifted it up ; it was very heavy. He opened it slowly and inside he found a number of gold pieces. He took them out, and at the bottom of the purse he found a small piece of paper on which was written in tiny lettering :

> Tak' the goud and buy a koo,
> You minded us, we've minded you.

Crawford went off next morning, without telling his wife, to see a rich farmer who lived near Kinross and, with some of the gold pieces the fairies had given him, he bought two cows.

It occurred to Crawford, as he was driving the cattle in front of him on the way home, that really he was no better off now than before. These cows, too, would die. He had no water for them to drink, no grass on which to feed them.

' What am I going to do ? ' he groaned.

' Take them away to Gowan Dell,' a thousand voices seemed to whisper in the air above his head.

' What ? What was that ? Did someone speak ? ' cried out Crawford.

' Take them away, take them away to Gowan Dell,' chorused the voices.

Crawford knew Gowan Dell as a desolate spot where only briars and weeds grew out of the stony, infertile ground. The idea of driving cows to this spot was laughable. Many another man would have laughed aloud at the suggestion, but Crawford was wise enough and kind enough not to offend the little people.

If no good could come of it, no harm could come either, and it wasn't far out of his way.

'Get up there, get along there,' he shouted at the cows, as he made them change direction.

When he reached Gowan Dell, Crawford stared dumbfounded at the scene in front of him. The briar bushes and weeds had disappeared ; in their place was a crop of rich, lush green grass, at which the cows immediately started munching.

Crawford drove his cattle daily to the Dell, week after week, month after month and, although there still had been no rain, the grass here never withered nor grew bare. Each cow yielded between sixteen and eighteen pints of milk a day, and the butter made from the milk was the finest that had ever been tasted in the county. Its fame spread far and wide, and people even came from other counties to buy it.

The neighbours were jealous of Crawford. They told each other that Gowan Dell was not Crawford's private property, and why should they not take their cows to feed there ? The good Crawford had no objection to this. Indeed, he was anxious that everyone should benefit from his own good fortune. But they didn't benefit, only Crawford's cows gave milk ; the fairies saw to that. However, the drought finally ended, and there was no more need for the magic effects of Gowan Dell. Crawford continued to take his cows there, and he continued to prosper as he had never done before. He has been dead for more than a hundred years now, but Gowan Dell is the same today as it was on that morning when his two new cows first set their hooves in it. And who would believe that it had ever been any different ?

Stine Bheag o' Tarbat ✌️

LONG ago there lived in the district of Tarbat Ness an old woman who was a famous witch. She was called Stine Bheag o' Tarbat, and was particularly famous for the power she had over the seas and winds. She could be of great help or great hindrance to the men of the sea who pleased or annoyed her. One ship's master who had offended her moored his ship one evening in a rocky bay. Next morning when he went on deck, he found that during the night the vessel had been mysteriously lifted over sea, rocks and beach, and now lay in a deep ditch, with a meadow on one side of it and two cornfields on the other. He hastened to Stine Bheag to apologise for whatever it was he had done to annoy her, and that night, in the same mysterious way, his boat was returned to her moorings in the sea. It was not often that Stine Bheag herself was tricked, but it was said that a farmer whom she had long annoyed by turning herself into a black beetle and humming about him, did once manage to catch her, and kept her confined for four days in his snuff-box !

Once, some men from Cromarty were fishing in the region of Tarbat Ness when they were troubled by a storm that blew up and prevented them from returning to their homes. They were forced to land their boat and strike camp on the land. The storm continued for two weeks. The rain put out their fires and soaked through the canvas of their tent. Except for the salted fish, their food was ruined. They were kept awake at night by the noise of the rain and wind, and every morning they saw the

131

mountainous rollers still heaving across the sea while the black clouds, heavy with rain, moved endlessly over the sky from the south-west.

'We can't go on like this,' grumbled one of the fishermen. 'We must have a change of wind.'

'If you blow hard enough,' joked another, 'perhaps we'll get it.'

'There's only one way to get a change of wind quickly,' interrupted a tall, strong young fellow by the name of MacGlashan, 'and that's by going to Stine Bheag and asking her to do something about it.'

'Stine Bheag!' exclaimed the first man. 'She won't do it for nothing, you know.'

'Aye, I know that, Sandy, but if we make a collection, we could pay her. What do you think about it, Jock?'

The third of the trio agreed with MacGlashan. 'And anyway we can't stay here much longer with nothing to eat and drink,' he said.

The other men were consulted, and it was agreed that MacGlashan, Sandy and Jock should visit the witch. Money was collected from each of the men before they left. Some gave willingly, but others put their hands in their pockets rather reluctantly.

The three men set off for the hovel where the witch lived. This was on the shore of a little sandy bay on the Dornoch Firth side of the Ness. It was one of what had once been a row of four cottages; the others were ruined and deserted, roofs fallen, paintwork bleached by the sea winds, and floors carpeted by weeds and sea-thrift. Stine Bheag's looked almost as neglected, but the men recognised it by the volume of black smoke that was belching forth from its chimney.

'It is said that Stine's relations once lived in these other cottages,' said MacGlashan in a low voice, 'but they quarrelled with her, and one day, when they were out in their boats, she called up a hurricane which drove them on to a quicksand where they perished.'

Jock and Sandy shivered. 'Let's go back,' suggested Jock.

'I don't much fancy meeting the old crone,' said Sandy nervously.

'Now we've walked all this way, we're going through with it,' said MacGlashan. 'Don't forget, we need that change of wind and we need it badly.'

He walked boldly up to the door which hung half open, and tapped against it. There was a loud cracking noise inside the house, like a series of shots from a pistol, that made it impossible for the tapping to be heard. He tapped louder, but the cracking went on, so he opened the door and, stooping a little, went through the low doorway. The cottage was full of smoke. He could dimly see a red glow at the hearth, and the old hag sitting on a stool, throwing handfuls of dried seaweed into the fire. As the bubbles of weed burst in the heat, they made the cracking noise that he had heard outside. Stine accompanied her actions with a steady murmur of Gaelic rhyme and, as the flames shot up, MacGlashan could see her long, thin face, white as snow, with scarcely any flesh on the bones, and the eyes burning in their sockets like the coals on the fire. Some of her wild grey hair had escaped from the red scarf she wore on her head, and tumbled to her shoulders, around which she wore a piece of tartan, fastened by a large silver brooch. Stine Bheag looked every inch the witch she was.

'Terrible weather we're having,' spoke up MacGlashan boldly.

The witch looked up at him, startled and angry.

' I have come,' went on MacGlashan, ' from a spot where my companions and I have been windbound for two weeks. We're frozen with the cold, and half-starved with hunger. We have heard of your remarkable powers, and were wondering if perhaps you would favour us with a change of wind—a wind that would take us back home safely to Cromarty.'

The old woman did not reply instantly, so MacGlashan thrust into her claw-like hands the coins he and his companions had collected. Her flesh was like sandpaper to his touch. She spread out her palms to the firelight and gazed scornfully, first at the coins, and then at MacGlashan.

' You expect me to help you in return for these few miserable coins ! ' she almost spat at him, her hoarse voice rising to a shriek.

' These are bad times, Mother, for we fisherfolk,' said MacGlashan. ' It's all the money we have. But we won't forget you, once we reach home safely.'

The witch appeared to go into a trance.

' Send one of your companions for the large water jug,' she said, at last.

MacGlashan gazed at her in wonder. How did she know he had brought companions with him ? They were still outside. And how did she know they had a large water jug at the place where they had camped ?

He went to the door. ' Hey, Jock, Sandy ! ' he called, ' come this way, lads.'

The two men entered Stine Bheag's dwelling place.

' Run back to the camp, Sandy,' said MacGlashan, ' and bring us the large water jug.'

When Sandy had gone, MacGlashan and Jock sat themselves down on a plank in the middle of the floor, and studied their

134

The witch ignored them

surroundings. In one corner there was a huge wooden trough, filled with water, from which came a bubbling, splashing noise, as if it contained live fish. At the side of it sat a large black cat. On a roughly made table were a few dried herbs, the skeleton of some animal and a staff with the tail of a fish fastened to one end, and the wings of a raven to the other. The men looked around them and occasionally whispered to each other. The witch ignored them, her head bent and her eyes fixed on the fire. After an hour or so, she suddenly jumped to her feet, scowled at MacGlashan as she caught him staring at her, clutched at some more seaweed and flung it on the fire, which momentarily dimmed. Jock shuddered in the darkness, but his companion was bold as ever.

' Och, Mother,' he said, ' you lead a terrible lonely life of it here.'

' Lonely ! How do you mean lonely ? ' she croaked.

As she spoke, a raven flew down from the rafters and alighted on her shoulder.

' Let's get out of here, Mac,' begged Jock, ' and see what's keeping Sandy.'

The words were scarcely out of his mouth when Sandy entered with the water jug, which Stine instantly seized from him.

' And now, she said, ' you must get out of here, all three of you. Wait at the rock yonder on the beach till I call you.'

MacGlashan and his friends waited for nearly half an hour, huddling together behind the rock, trying to keep warm. Night was falling and the ruined cottages looked even more dismal than before. There glimmered a dull red light through the window of Stine Bheag's hovel, and now and again shadows of persons appeared to pass between the window and the fire.

At last the door opened, and the harsh voice of Stine was

heard calling them. MacGlashan stepped up to her, and took the water jug which was held out to him. He noticed that the top of the jug was stopped up with a bunch of straw.

'What must we do, Stine?' asked MacGlashan.

'Set sail at dawn tomorrow,' she said. 'But be warned: don't touch the straw in the neck of this jug until you have reached Cromarty.'

MacGlashan assured her that they would do as she said, and he and his companions returned to camp.

The wind lowered that night, and some of the fishermen were anxious to launch the boat immediately, but MacGlashan told them what the witch had said and, with some impatience, they waited until morning. At dawn the Moray Firth looked as still and as glassy as a mirror. The tent was dismantled, the boat launched, and the men were at the oars before the sun had risen. A light breeze rose from the north-east—just such a breeze as they wanted. The sails were hoisted, and soon the boat was scudding for home.

'It's a wonderful thing to be sure,' cried out one of the crew. 'What could Stine Bheag have put in the water jug to work this miracle?'

'She's an evil woman,' said another. 'They won't like it in Cromarty when they know we've had dealings with the likes of her. I'm thinking Mac had better take out the straw from the jug before we land.'

'Then pass up the jug to me,' said MacGlashan. 'After all, we're nearly there now, it can't do much harm.'

Foolish MacGlashan to disobey Stine Bheag's orders! He pulled out the straw and flung it over his head into the sea. Half a dozen heads peered into the bottle; there appeared to be nothing inside it.

' For heaven's sake, lads,' shouted the man at the bows, ' what have you done there ? Lower the sails ! There's a squall blowing up from landwards. Quick !—or we'll go down like a mussel-shell.'

The crew hastened to the sails, and managed to get them down before the squall struck the boat with the fury of a tornado. The men rushed to their oars, but had scarcely taken the first stroke when the oars were torn out of their hands by the force of the hurricane. The waters churned around them, the wind howled continuously, the waves were so high that the land they had hoped to reach in a few minutes was now hidden from view. Land, bay, cliffs and villages receded as the boat drifted helplessly in the direction from which it had come. Before noon, the crew had landed at Tarbat Ness, where they found Stine Bheag sitting on the shore, occasionally chanting to herself, and chuckling in between times.

' And what's brought you here, my bonny young men ? ' she asked, although it was fairly obvious that she had been expecting them.

' Ah, Mother,' groaned MacGlashan, ' that cursed straw ! '

' I'd imprisoned the winds you didn't want in that bottle,' said the witch. ' It gave me a lot of trouble. When you took out the straw, you released your enemy. Ah well, it's your own fault. I did my best for you. Now you'll have to take the road home.'

' We can't do that, Mother,' replied MacGlashan. ' What would we do with our fish ? '

The witch shook her grey locks at him. The other men cowered away from her. But still MacGlashan was not frightened.

Try again,' he pleaded. ' Imprison the winds again. Put more straw in the bottle-neck. We won't walk the road. If you don't help us, we'll stay here in the ruined cottages until the better weather comes in the spring.'

' No, no, you mustn't do that,' cried out Stine angrily. ' I don't want strangers here.'

' We'd interfere too much in your witchcraft, wouldn't we ? ' taunted MacGlashan. ' We'd find out too much about your secrets, wouldn't we ? '

The old woman stamped on the sand with rage and shook her clenched fist at him. MacGlashan stood his ground, and again insisted that they would stay if she didn't help them. At last, the witch sulkily agreed to do what she could.

The fishermen arrived at Cromarty the following morning without any further adventures. The straws stayed in the water bottle, and the story of how Stine Bheag o' Tarbat had helped them stayed untold by those few fortunate fishermen who, after that day, always had good weather when they went out to gather their portion of the harvest of the sea.

The Meal Mill at Eathie 🪶

IT was a small mill with an old-fashioned horizontal water-wheel of so little power that a man once stopped it with his shoulder that he might rescue his bonnet which had fallen on the stones in the stream. Nevertheless, it was a celebrated mill. No-one lived near it, and there were few men in the country who cared to approach it after sunset. The miller's house was some distance from it and, although he spent the hours of dark at his home, the wheels of the mill could often be heard at night, creaking and turning, as if a host of people were working inside. Once, the miller, who had remained at work later than usual, was surprised to hear outside the neighing and champing of horses and the rattling of carts. He went outside and saw a long train of small carts, laden with sacks and drawn by miniature ponies. The ponies were being urged on by little men, about three feet in height, dressed in grey, with scarlet caps on their heads. The line of ponies, carts and little men appeared to have come out of a square opening in a steep cliff opposite the mill. The miller was greatly alarmed, but so were the little men : no sooner had the nearer figures noticed him than they uttered shrill screams, and the ponies and carts moved quickly backwards through the opening in the cliff, which shut over them silently and completely, like the curtain coming down at the end of a play.

The miller called at the local inn that evening, and told his

139

strange story to his friends and neighbours. A wild young fellow called Tam M'Kechan—who was a bit of a rogue and often in trouble with the law—listened scornfully to the miller's tale.

' You'd been having a drink or two in that mill of yours, I'd say,' he scoffed.

' I'd been working hard, which is something you wouldn't understand,' retorted the miller. ' That's why I was in the mill so late.'

' Well then, you have a very pretty imagination,' laughed Tam. ' It makes a good story, I'll say that much for you. Little horses and fairy attendants indeed ! '

' Everyone knows strange things happen at the meal mill at Eathie, don't they ? ' The miller appealed to the rest of the company, who readily agreed that this was so. ' I can tell you it was a very alarming experience,' he said.

' It wouldn't worry me to spend a night at the mill, with no other companion than my pipes,' said Tam. Few could match Tam M'Kechan at the bagpipes.

' You're a bold man, then,' said the miller.

' Aye, I'm a bold man,' agreed Tam boastfully.

Arrangements were then made for Tam to spend a night at the Eathie mill. The next day the miller invited a young farmer called Jock Hossack, who was in love with Tam's sister, to spend the early part of the evening with them. They spent an hour or two together in the miller's cottage before setting off for the mill. Jock was a kind-hearted lad, and he didn't much like the idea of his future brother-in-law going into any sort of danger.

' I've been thinking, Tam,' he said, ' that you would be better leaving the good fairy people alone.'

'What!—and let the miller think I'm afraid.' Tam shook his head.

'Well, since you're bent on playing the fool, let me play it with you,' said Jock. 'I'll wrap myself in my plaid and stay at the mill with you. You can play to me on your pipes to keep me in good spirits.'

'No, no, Jock Hossack,' said Tam. 'I'll keep my good music for the good fairy people. You may come as far as the edge of the burn with me tonight, and tomorrow, as early in the morning as you like, you may come to the mill to fetch me.'

Tam wrapped his plaid round him, took his pipes under his arm, and, accompanied by Jock and the miller, set out for the dell in which the mill was situated. He left his companions on the far bank of the mill-stream, and they stood there for a while until they could see he had lit a fire in the mill. As they left, they heard the shrill notes of his pibroch against the background of the rushing waters of the stream.

The first watery rays of the morning sun had just touched the mill when Jock and the miller pushed open the mill door next day. All was silent within. There was nothing but a heap of white ashes in the hearth, although a pile of logs lay untouched beside it. The stool on which Tam had probably been sitting lay overturned in front of the dead fire. There was no sign of Tam. Weeks passed and still there was no sign of Tam. The neighbours forgot him, but Jock could not do so. He wanted to solve the mystery, and decided to spend a night in the mill himself.

The first few hours of the evening passed slowly. He piled wood high on the fire until the mill was bright with fire-flame and every rafter and beam was visible in the light. Jock yawned and closed his eyes. A sudden cry disturbed him as, with a flutter of wings, one of the miller's plump ducks came swooping down towards the fire.

' Poor bird ! ' exclaimed Jock. ' It escapes the fox to fall into the fire, and I had almost forgotten how hungry I am.'

He killed the duck, plucked and cleaned it and then suspended it on a piece of string before the fire, twirling it round and round as if it were on a spit. A delicious smell filled the mill, as the fat from the duck hissed and spluttered on the hot coals. Jock had forgotten about the fairies as he prepared his supper, but a sudden burst of music from outside reminded him. He rose quickly from the hearth.

' That might be the music of Tam's pipes,' he said to himself. He gave another twirl to the duck, and went over to a window.

The moon was mirrored in the waters of the stream and was like a spotlight on the smooth green sward at the edge. The grass was crowded with tiny figures, many of whom were dancing merrily. The music was not of Tam's making, so, leaving the little creatures to their merry-making, Jock returned to the fire.

He had scarcely sat down on his stool when there was a low tap at the door, followed by a second and a third. Jock continued to turn his duck. He didn't want visitors, certainly not of the fairy sort, and was determined not to admit them. However, though the door was bolted and barred, it fell open on the fourth tap, and there entered a funny little figure with the wrinkled face of an old man and the sprightly limbs of a young boy.

' What's your name, man ? ' asked the gnome, coming up close to Jock until their noses were almost touching.

' What's your name, eh ? ' he asked again, when Jock did not reply.

Jock was annoyed by his abrupt manner, and had no intention of replying properly to the question.

142

'*Mysel' an' Mysel'*,' he said mysteriously—meaning '*myself*'.

'Ah, *Mysel' an' Mysel'*, is it? Well, that's a funny name,' said the little man. 'What's that you've got there, *Mysel' an' Mysel'*?'

He touched the duck with the tip of one long finger, and dabbed a spot of scalding grease on Jock's cheek.

'I said, what's that you've got there, *Mysel' an' Mysel'*?' He dabbed Jock's other cheek with more scalding grease.

At this, Jock lost his temper. Scarcely thinking of what might happen to him afterwards, he shouted, 'What is it, indeed?' and dashed the bird, with a full swing of his arm, against the face of the intruder. 'It's that!' cried out Jock.

The little creature screamed out in pain and fury. The music stopped instantly outside. Jock Hossack had scarcely time to add fresh fuel to the fire, which was nearly out, before crowds of fairy men came swarming round the mill. Their figures appeared at every door, their faces at every window.

'Who did it, Sanachy—who did it?' came the cry from a thousand fairy throats.

'Oh, 'twas *Mysel' an' Mysel'*,' screeched the little man. ''Twas *Mysel' an' Mysel'*.'

'And if it was yoursel' an' yoursel' who did it, poor Sanachy,' replied his companions, 'who's to blame for that but you?'

They still clustered round the mill, and Jock was afraid that, as soon as the little man had had time to explain what he meant, there would be further trouble. He had given himself up for lost, when a cock crowed outside. A breeze blew up which moaned and sighed for a few seconds and, when it had died down, Jock found himself alone. He thanked his good fortune and hurried home, determined to marry Tam's sister and to worry about Tam no longer.

There were those who said that Tam returned from fairyland seven years after his mysterious disappearance. And this may well be true, as one Thomas M'Kechan was sentenced at Perth for sheep stealing a few months after the seven years were up !

The Fisherman and the Seal Maid ⚓

O N the west coast of Sutherland there were once some people
known as *Sliochd na Maighdean Chuain*, which, translated,
means, 'the children of the mermaid', and this is the story of
their beginning.

A handsome young fisherman was walking down the beach
towards his fishing boat when he glimpsed among the waves the
face of the most beautiful woman he had ever seen. She would
disappear under the water for a few minutes, and then there she
would be again, her long hair floating over her white shoulders
as she bobbed up on the crest of the waves. The fisherman knew
that this was no human maiden, but he had fallen in love with her,
and also knew that she was the only woman he would ever want
for his wife. But he had to be careful; any daughter of the Sea
King might easily lure him to a cave at the bottom of the ocean,
from which he might never escape. So he hid himself behind a
rock and waited. When the mermaid thought she was alone,
she came ashore. Now, this was actually no ordinary mermaid
but a seal maid, and, on the lower part of her body up to her
waist, instead of a tail, she had a sealskin coat. The fisherman
watched as she removed this, put it on a rock near by, and then
slipped back into the sea for another swim. The fisherman
seized this opportunity to come out from his hiding place, picked
up the sealskin and put it under his jacket.

As soon as she came ashore again, the maid searched wildly for her missing skin. She wandered up and down the beach, moaning and crying.

'Without my sealskin I cannot get back to my ocean home,' she wailed. 'Oh, where can it be? Where can it be?'

The young fisherman went up to her, and tried to comfort her, but he did not tell her he had stolen her sealskin.

'Why don't you come home with me?' he asked. 'I will marry you. I have a nice little house and I am a good fisherman. We could be very happy.'

The mermaid shook her head woefully. She wanted only to return to her own home at the bottom of the sea. But without her sealskin, what could she do? The fisherman was handsome and kind so, at last, she dried her tears and accepted his offer. She followed him quietly and obediently to his white-washed cottage. And after she had married him, she was always a quiet and obedient wife. She mended the fisherman's nets, she kept the house spotlessly clean and she cooked his meals well. But she had left her laughter behind in the green depths of the sea, and even when she smiled—which she seldom did—her eyes stayed still and dark with sorrow and longing for her own folk. Sometimes she would go down to the seashore and stand on the edge of the water which lapped over her small white feet and seemed to call her gently home. Or she would sit on the pebbles and sing the weird sea-songs of her childhood. And often she would roam up and down the beach, up and down, hunting behind the rocks on which the winkles clung, in the caves where the patterned sea-shells lay, and in the little pools where the crabs scuttled and the sea-anemones curled and uncurled in the clear water. But she never found her sealskin.

In a way, she loved her husband, but not as much as he loved

Sometimes she would go down to the seashore

her. They had children and, in a way, she loved them too, but not as much as she loved the memory of her seal brothers and her seal sisters.

When their father was out fishing one wet day, the children were playing in the barn.

' Here, help me to move this,' cried the eldest boy, pointing to a large wooden crate which lay in a corner. ' If we put it in the centre of the barn, we can pretend it's a boat, and that we are grown fishermen like our father.'

They had begun to pull it away from the wall, when one of the younger children spotted a strange-looking skin which was hidden behind the crate.

' Look at this funny thing ! ' he called out to his brothers and sisters. They crowded round him while he pranced about with the skin draped across his shoulders.

' Let's show it to our mother,' suggested one of the little girls. ' Perhaps she will be able to tell us what it is.'

And the children ran into the house where their mother was cooking the dinner.

' Look, Mother,' said the boy who had found the skin, ' what we discovered in the barn. Do you know what it is ? '

The mermaid turned round from the fire and, as soon as she saw what the child was holding in his hands, she gave a great cry of joy, seized it from him and rushed out of the house. She ran down towards the sea, and the children ran after her. When she reached the beach, she pulled on the sealskin and, without so much as a backward glance at her children, she plunged into the sea with a glad shout and disappeared under the waves.

On his return that evening, the fisherman found his children huddled together in the house, crying for their mother. They told him what had happened, and he knew that he had lost his beloved wife for ever. He tried to explain to the children that their mother was really a mermaid, and he told the eldest girl that henceforth she would have to take her mother's place in the house.

The fisherman never saw his wife again, although he often went down to the rocks and sat there, looking out to sea, and calling for her. She didn't entirely forget her children, however, and, when her sons grew up and became fishermen like their father, they always caught more and better fish than their neighbours.

' Ah yes, those *Slioch na Maighdean Chuain*,' it was said, ' their mother drives the fish to their hooks, it's no wonder they do so well.'

Sometimes she even spoke to her children, and her sons occasionally caught a glimpse of her when they were out in their boats. She gave them all sorts of strange advice, and once made a puzzling remark which none of them really understood.

' Never drink sea water without putting it through a sieve,' she said, ' as there is many a living creature in the ocean.'

148

She certainly continued to have a mother's interest in her children, and they knew they could always rely upon her to come to their help. Once only she returned to land, and that was when she felt the weakest of her sons needed her.

Rory was a simple boy, feeble in mind yet strong in body. He was not a fisherman like his brothers but worked in a mill where he helped the miller to move the bags of grain. The miller was usually very patient with him, but one day, when he was in a bad humour, Rory, in his slow, clumsy way, crossed his path as he was hurrying through the mill to attend to some urgent business. The miller gave the lad a push, shouting at him, ' Out of my way, you stupid fool ! '

Rory, who was carrying a sack of grain on his back, slipped and went sprawling on the floor where he lay, roaring at the miller.

' I'll tell my mother about you,' he cried, ' that's what I'll do. She'll pay you out for this, you see if she doesn't.'

He went on roaring and shouting, and nothing the miller said would calm him. Meanwhile, about half a mile away, the mermaid mother heard the cry of her son. She hurried out of the sea, removed her sealskin and, with only the long dripping seaweed for clothing, she made her way to the mill. The astonished miller soon found himself face to face with an angry mermaid.

' How dare you hurt my son Rory, a grandson of the Sea King ? ' she demanded. And she opened her mouth and squirted a stream of boiling water at him. He narrowly escaped being scalded to death and, as he ran screaming into his house, the mermaid took Rory by the hand and led him away.

Neither the boy nor his mother went back to the mill, and neither the mill nor the miller prospered again. Mermaids, like the fairies, make good friends but bad enemies.

Andrew and the Mermaid

ANOTHER young man who fell in love with a mermaid was one, Andrew, who lived in the far north of Scotland. One morning, when he was walking along the seashore, he heard singing. It was very early and he hadn't expected to find anyone else on the beach. For a moment he thought that the music he heard was made by the incoming tide as it filled up the little rocky pools, but he stopped and listened and, again, heard someone singing. He glanced around and, at first, all he could see were the white sea-horses as they chased each other in a long frothy line along the beach. But, as he walked on, he saw that there was someone sitting on a rock at the far end of the bay. And as he drew nearer, he realised that he was looking at a mermaid. She was combing her hair with a mother-of-pearl comb, and singing as she did so. Her voice was as sweet as the nightingale's, her hair gold as buttercups, her skin white as sea foam and her eyes as green as the waters of her homeland. Andrew could see the reflection of her lovely face in the mirror which she held in one hand. He approached and put his arms round her. She gave a cry, dropped her comb and mirror, and turned round to look at Andrew. From that moment they were in love. They talked together ; the mermaid promised to meet him in the same spot on the following day. Then, with a flick of her tail, she dived into the sea and was lost to his sight.

The next morning she had with her a handful of what looked to Andrew like coloured glass.

Gray fixed an arrow to his bow

'Here, take these,' said the mermaid. 'They are a present for you, to show you that I love you.'

Andrew examined the gift, and found the mermaid had given him a collection of amethysts and rubies which glistened and flashed as the rays of the early morning sun shone down upon them.

'Where did you get these?' he asked.

'I found them when I was swimming among the wrecks of the many boats that lie at the bottom of the Pentland Firth,' she replied.

Andrew visited his nearest town later that week, and sold the jewels. Neighbours wondered why he suddenly changed his way of life. He moved to a bigger house, dressed in finer clothes, ate richer food, drank more expensive wines. And, almost daily, he met the mermaid who loved him so dearly. But he was extravagant and his newly found riches dwindled.

'I need more jewels,' he said to the mermaid. 'Are there more to be found in the Pentland Firth?'

She told him the supply was almost endless, and the next time they met, she poured into his lap topazes like the eyes of tigers, sapphires like the eyes of Siamese cats, and emeralds like the eyes of her sister mermaids.

'How generous you are, and how lovely you are!' exclaimed Andrew, embracing her warmly.

But the richer he became, the more Andrew entertained his friends and neighbours, and the more he entertained, the more he neglected his mermaid lover.

One day she brought him a wonderful collection of diamonds.

'I do not know how to thank you,' said Andrew. 'They are like the dew-drops of the ocean.'

'They are like my tears will be if you are unfaithful to me,' said the mermaid sadly.

Andrew had so much money from the sale of the other jewels, he did not need to sell the diamonds. Instead, he gave some of them to beautiful ladies of his acquaintance whom he wished to impress, and they wore them in brooches and rings, or dangling from their ears.

When next he met the mermaid, she upbraided him for his infidelity.

'Ah, Andrew!' she sighed. 'Why do you give away my presents to my rivals?'

Andrew denied that he had done so but, that very night, he gave one of the largest of the diamonds to the most beautiful lady in the district.

Again the mermaid upbraided him for his infidelity. And, after that, she and Andrew had many lovers' quarrels. The mermaid was very unhappy and determined that none of her human rivals should take her lover from her.

One day Andrew went to the seashore to keep his appointment with her, and found she was not sitting on her usual rock. So he sat down on it, and waited for her. Soon he saw a lovely boat coming towards him from the west. It glided swiftly through the still water like sharp scissors cutting through silk. The mermaid was at the prow. She called out to him, and he plunged into the sea, swam out to the boat and clambered aboard.

'This is a new way you come to me,' he said.

'I want to take you away,' replied the mermaid.

'I don't think I want to go away, thank you,' said Andrew, thinking of the comfortable life he now had at home.

'I could take you to a cave at Duncansby Head,' coaxed the mermaid.

ANDREW AND THE MERMAID

'I don't want to go to Duncansby Head, thank you,' said Andrew.

'In that cave,' said the mermaid, ignoring her lover's refusal, 'I keep all the treasure that has ever been lost in the Firth. What I have brought you so far is but a glimpse of the wonders that lie in my cave at Duncansby Head.'

'Are you sure about this?' asked Andrew. 'You are not making up tales to deceive me, are you?'

The mermaid assured him that she was telling the truth. The prospect of such wealth was too much for the greedy young man, and he said he would go with her.

The boat had neither sails nor oars yet it swept through the water as if by magic while the mermaid kept her hand on the tiller. It was not long before they reached the entrance of a huge cave. The mermaid dropped overboard a silver anchor, and she and Andrew disembarked and entered the gloomy room of rock. Andrew began to feel sleepy and slid down on to the sandy floor where, with his head on a small boulder, he fell fast asleep. He did not know how long he slept but, when he awoke, the moonlight had made a silver path through the cave, lighting up the glittering piles of precious stones which lay in profusion at the far end. Andrew arose and rushed towards the nearest pile of treasure to discover how many of the stones he could manage to take away with him. It was not until he had dipped his hands deep into a myriad of ice-cold diamonds that he realised his wrists were bound by slender golden chains that were long enough for him to reach the jewels but not long enough to allow him to wander beyond the entrance of the cave. He looked round desperately for the mermaid whom, until now, he had completely forgotten. She was sitting on a seaweed-covered log that had been pulled across the mouth of the cave.

' Why am I chained ? ' asked Andrew. ' Is this some sort of a joke ? '

The mermaid shook her buttercup hair at him.

' I cannot trust you to be faithful to me. You broke the invisible chain which bound you to me ; you will not be able to break these chains so easily. I will visit you and care for you, but you will stay here with only the jewels you prize so highly for company. You are mine for evermore and there is no escape.'

And, as far as I know, Andrew is still confined in a cave, full of treasure, somewhere near Duncansby Head.

John Reid and the Mermaid ❧

JOHN REID was a shipmaster who owned a large sloop with which he traded between Holland and the northern ports of Scotland. He was lucky in business and grew wealthy as the years went by. He should have been a happy man but, in fact, he was one of the unhappiest men alive because he was in love with the beautiful Helen Stuart who was not in love with him. She was many years younger than he, and after they had first met, he thought of her all day and dreamed of her all night. She only vaguely remembered a pleasant, good-humoured man, broad-shouldered and with skin tanned to a deep bronze. The months passed and John Reid still thought of Helen Stuart. Towards the end of April, he returned from one of his trips, determined to have another glimpse of the lady. He knew that on May-day she would be out with her companions, gathering May-dew, so he rose early that day and wandered along the seashore. The stars disappeared one by one, and the sun rose and flung a path of flame across the water. But John Reid did not stop to admire the beauty of the dawn, he could think only of Helen Stuart.

As he clambered over the rocks, he heard the low notes of a song. He looked around him to see if a fisherman in a boat was passing by or a shepherd whistling on the hillside, but he could only see a huge bull seal that had raised its head above the waves as if it, too, were listening to the music. When John reached the other side of the rocks, he saw the singer. It was a young girl sitting half on a rock, half in the water. Her long hair fell thickly on her creamy shoulders and, as she pulled herself up on to the rock, the sun shone on her lower half with such brightness that the sailor had to shield his eyes for a moment.

'The sun glitters thus on fish that are freshly caught,' murmured John to himself. 'Of course—she is a mermaid ! It is the scales of her tail that shine so brightly.'

He would have pretended he had not seen her and gone on his way, had he not suddenly remembered that mermaids have strange powers. Perhaps this one could help to make Helen Stuart love him.

He crept in and out of the rocks until he was behind her. She turned round, and the last note of her song changed to a shriek of alarm. She tried to fling herself into the water, but John Reid had locked his brawny arms firmly round her fishy waist. She struggled with the strength of a whale. John's muscles quivered with the strain of holding her and, had not the thought of Helen Stuart kept him firm, he would have let go. The mermaid's struggles became fainter and fainter until he was able to drag her farther up the beach.

'Man, what do you want with me ?' she asked weakly in a voice which, though as sweet as the song of a bird, was sea-cold like the bottom of the ocean.

'Three wishes,' said John Reid, remembering what was supposed to be the correct answer to such a question.

'Speak on,' said the mermaid.

'My father, a sailor like myself,' said John, 'was drowned many years ago. My first wish is that neither I, nor any of my friends, shall be drowned at sea. My second wish is that I shall continue to prosper as I have done recently. My third wish is that Helen Stuart, whom I love, shall, in turn, love me.'

156

' Quit, and have,' replied the mermaid.

John Reid released his hold on her. Pressing her tail against a rock until it curled to her waist, she shot into the sea like an uncoiled spring. A slight ripple splashed against the beach. All trace of the mermaid had vanished. John wiped his brow and, with hope in his heart, climbed up the hill, at the top of which he expected to find Helen. And there she was, sitting with a friend on the grass, near a spot appropriately known as Lover's Leap. Fortune had already begun to favour the sailor.

' Fancy seeing you here, John Reid ! ' exclaimed Helen's companion. ' Helen has been telling us of a dream she had last night. She dreamt she was gathering May-dew, but the grass and bushes were dry and she had collected only a few drops when she heard someone singing near the rocks on the shore. Then she saw you asleep on the beach and the singer, a lovely lady, by your side. Helen was afraid you would not wake before the tide covered you, but suddenly you were standing beside her, and began to help her shake the bushes for dew. She looked for the singing lady and saw her far out on the sea, floating on the waves like a white seagull. As she wondered at this, she heard the drops of water which you had shaken down, tinkling against the bottom of her bucket. And, just imagine, John Reid, the drops had turned into pieces of pure gold ! '

' That is quite true,' said Helen. ' But the strangest part of it all is that, as we passed up the slope this morning, I heard among the rocks on the beach the same song which I heard in my dream. I hope now you are going to fill our buckets with gold.'

She laughed and John laughed, too.

' You may have heard the magic music,' he said, ' but I have seen and talked with the singer. She is a mermaid.'

' Seen and talked with the mermaid ! ' cried Helen's friend.

'Heaven forbid ! The last time she appeared was a few days before that terrible storm in which you lost your father. Take care not to repeat her words, for they thrive ill who carry tales from the other world to this.'

'Don't worry,' replied John. 'I am the mermaid's master ; I had the better of her. I have no need to be afraid.'

And he went on to tell his story. He told them only two of his three wishes, but there was a gleam in Helen's eyes that suggested she guessed the nature of the third. She listened to him in wonder and admiration and, when she realised the danger he had been in, her heart filled with love for him. They walked home together, Helen leaning on the sailor's arm for support and protection. And by next May-day they were man and wife.

The Dropping-Cave

THE Dropping-Cave is so called because the water from the springs inside it continually drips slowly upon such mosses and grasses that grow there, until at last they turn into stone. The long narrow cave appears to have no ending, and a pebble flung into it rebounds from side to side of the rock until it falls with a hollow thud in the far distance, as if it had been thrown into the depths of the sea. Stalactites and stalagmites make a weird palace of wonder out of it.

Boatmen, sailing inshore at night, used sometimes to see a faint blue light shining at the entrance. A mermaid was once seen sitting outside it, combing her hair and singing a sad song. A man, hunting for crabs on the seashore and returning late by way of the cave, nearly turned to stone, like the mosses and grasses, when he saw the ghost of an old grey-headed man, with a beard that reached his waist, sitting outside the cave, gazing wistfully towards the sea.

Such were some of the tales of terror that were told of this mysterious cave. And, until Willie Miller decided to do so, no man had ever dared to explore its strange interior. His friends tried to dissuade him, but Willie was determined. He wanted to find out what was in the cave and how many miles underground it went. He sewed sprigs of rowan and wych-elm in the hem of his waistcoat to protect him from evil spirits, thrust a Bible into one pocket and a bottle of whisky into the other. He took a torch in one hand, and a thick wooden staff in the other, and set out for the cave on a fine midsummer's morning.

He reached the entrance of the cave, lit the torch, and, firmly grasping the staff, stepped boldly into the gloomy shadows. The cave narrowed and sloped deeper into the ground as Willie stumbled on. The floor was of a white stone like marble, and formed hollows here and there which were filled with water so pure that it sparkled in the light of Willie's torch. Huge clusters of white icicles hung from the roof, and the water trickled in channels at the side, tinkling into the hollows of the floor. Willie looked around him with so much interest that he missed his footing on the uneven floor and fell headlong, shattering his bottle of whisky against the side of the cave. Some of the liquor collected in a natural bowl and, not wanting to lose all benefit of it, Willie crouched on his knees and lapped it up.

When he got to his feet, he noticed that a rainbow had formed around his torch and a blue mist was arising in front of him. The cave was filled with a low humming noise like bees returning to their hive in the evening. On went the bold Willie. The cave widened. The white walls were ridged now and folded like lengths of material in a shop window, and myriads of crystals sparkled overhead. Willie's echoing footsteps resounded above the humming noise. The light of his torch showed him sheets of water and ribs of rock with arched corridors leading in many directions. Occasionally, as the main path turned upwards, he could hear the wind moaning in the trees above and the scream of a hawk as it pounced on its prey, and, once, he heard the blast of a smith's bellows and the clang of hammers on the anvil. He knew he must have walked a very long way inland to be under the blacksmith's forge. Down again sloped the marble floor—and on went Willie. All now seemed wild and unnatural. The humming had changed to a deep, hollow noise like the growling of some wild beast. The entire cave appeared to be swinging and turning until the floor stood upright and Willie fell against it. His torch fell into the water, hissed and sputtered and went out. Willie thought he saw a score of dark figures flitting around him before he lost consciousness.

When he recovered, Willie was no longer in darkness. A dim red light flickered on the walls and roof like the reflection of fire. He rose and staggered on, reminding himself that outside it was sunlight, and hoping that sooner or later he would find an opening and be able to walk home over the hills. The passage suddenly ended, and he found himself in a huge room, at the side of which a great waterfall thundered, and at the other side of which was a huge fire. In front of the fire lay a tomb of dark stone, and on top of this lay a bugle of gold. Willie could not resist lifting this to his mouth and giving a blast on it. The noise echoed and re-echoed in the room, down the corridors and back again. The waterfall stopped flowing, the fire died down. The lid of the tomb began to tremble and heave as if some giant were lifting it from below. In terror, Willie again blew the trumpet. The lid continued to move and a giant hand appeared under one corner of it, stretching out as if it would grasp hold of the stranger who had dared to enter the Dropping-Cave. Willie gave a scream, flung down the bugle and rushed towards the passage. A yell of rage came from the tomb as the cover settled over it. The waterfall flowed again. The fire sprang to life. A hurricane of wind and spray dashed Willie against the side of the rocks, but, with a tremendous effort, he managed to reach the passage. Running, walking, stumbling, crawling, Willie, half-crazed with fear, at last found himself back near the opening of the cave. He leapt out of it on to the beach and hurried home to tell his strange tale to his friends. None of them believed him, but, on the other hand, none of them dared find out the truth of it for themselves.

James Gray and the Clashnichd ❧

THERE was once a giant who lived in the wilds of Banffshire. He was a cruel and wicked giant who ill-treated his poor giant wife. He beat her every night, sometimes because she had not tidied the cave where they lived together, sometimes because the food she cooked for him did not meet with his satisfaction, and sometimes just because he felt like beating her. And every night the screams of the giantess—who was called the Clashnichd —could be heard ringing across the fields and hills. Her shrieks greatly disturbed James Gray, the tenant of a nearby farm. Night after night her cries and lamentations kept him and his family from their sleep, so that in the daytime James fell asleep in his fields, his wife fell asleep in her kitchen and their children fell asleep at their lessons. And no work was done at all.

James Gray was sleepily mending a hedge on the boundary of his land one day when he heard a sound like thunder. But there were no clouds in the sky and no sign of storm on the horizon. The thunder he heard was the noise of the footsteps of the Clashnichd who was out looking for food for her husband's dinner.

'Aha,' said James Gray, 'this is the chance I have been looking for.'

He shouted to the Clashnichd, whose head he could see over the trees of a copse a short distance away. The giantess slowly ambled towards him, pushing aside the tall trees as if they were small bramble bushes.

' Good afternoon, man,' boomed the Clashnichd, ' and what do you want with me ? '

' I have a complaint to make,' said James. ' My family and I are suffering greatly because of you.'

The Clashnichd said she was sorry about this and asked what she had done to annoy them.

' It's the terrible noise you make every night,' explained James. ' We can't get any sleep. Do you have to scream and roar like that every single night ? It's as if a thousand fiends were shouting down our ears. It's impossible for us to endure it much longer.'

When the Clashnichd explained to him why she made so much noise, James Gray felt more sympathetic towards her.

' My husband is a terrible man,' sighed the giantess, ' and I wish I could be rid of him.'

' Indeed, madam,' said James Gray, ' I wish you could, for then we might all have some peace.'

The Clashnichd and the farmer parted the best of friends. And the following night when the moon was full, the Clashnichd called at James's farm. She tapped on the back door, making the house rock on its foundations. James guessed immediately who was his visitor.

' What do you want ? ' he asked, opening the door. ' I can't ask you in because our house isn't big enough.'

' I want you to help me get rid of my husband,' said the giantess. ' You were very sympathetic when we met the other afternoon, and I have heard that you are an excellent marksman. If you can kill him, I shall receive no more beatings and you may get some sleep.'

' How may I kill him ? ' asked James Gray. ' It would be like setting an ant against an elephant.'

'My husband has a mole over his heart,' said the Clashnichd. 'If you can pierce that, he will die instantly.'

James Grey, desperate for want of sleep, agreed to do what he could. Armed with his bow and arrows and riding on the giantess's huge shoulders, he set out for the giant's cave. The giant stood at the opening of it, shouting and shaking his fist at them as they approached.

Gray fixed an arrow to his bow. From his perch on the Clashnichd's shoulders, he was about level with the giant's heart. He took careful aim at the enormous mole that was the size of a Scotsman's bonnet, pulled back the bowstring and released the arrow. It flew straight to the centre of its target. The giant gave a yell and vanished into thin air.

The Clashnichd danced with joy and happiness until James begged her to stop as it was very uncomfortable for him being jogged up and down on her shoulders. She put him down on the ground, saying to him, 'James Gray, you have done me great good this day. From now on, I shall devote my time and talents to your service and prosperity. What shall be my first task?'

James wasn't sure he wanted the services of the exuberant giantess; all he wanted was to get some sleep, which it seemed now he might be able to do. Thinking to get rid of the Clashnichd, he pointed out to her a herd of deer which were passing through the forest.

'There are my horses,' he said, 'which have escaped from the stable. Round them up and tether them again in the stable.'

The simple giantess set off on her task, and James Gray went home to his bed. His head had just touched the pillow when the house began to rock in a familiar way. The Clashnichd was 'tapping' at the back door.

James went wearily downstairs and opened up the door. The Clashnichd grinned hugely at him.

'I have stabled the horses,' she said, 'although I must say it wasn't easy ; they were very unruly. What shall I do now ?'

We are not told what James Gray replied, nor yet how long it was before the poor man managed to get a full night's sleep !

The Herdsman of Cruachan ❧

THE Herdsman of Cruachan had only one thing he prized higher than his shaggy dun filly, and that was his beloved wife. One evening, when he had finished work with his flocks, he returned to find that neither his wife nor his shaggy dun filly were anywhere about. It was not long before he discovered that the big giant, King of Sorcha, had stolen them away. He went to bed and lay there in the dark, making plans to get them back.

He made breakfast for himself when morning came, and set off in quest of his wife and the filly. He baked a bannock to take with him before he left. He walked a long way until his feet were through the soles of his shoes, and the birds had ceased singing and had gone to roost in the bushes and trees. The dark clouds of night were creeping over the sky as the light clouds of day were departing when the Herdsman saw a house not far away. He went in and sat down. There appeared to be no-one living there, although the fire was blazing, the house clean and a bed made with fresh linen. But before long, he was joined by the hawk of Glencuaich who said to him, ' Are you the Herdsman of Cruachan ? '

' I am,' he replied.

' Do you know who were here last night ? ' asked the hawk.

' I do not,' said the Herdsman.

' The big giant, the King of Sorcha, with your wife and the shaggy dun filly, and the giant was threatening that if he could get hold of you he would take off your head.'

'I well believe it,' said the Herdsman, shaking at the thought.

The hawk then gave him food and drink and sent him to bed. She rose in the morning, made breakfast for him, and baked a bannock for him to eat on his journey. Off he set once again. He saw another house that evening, and when he went in, here, too, there was a blazing fire, a clean room and a bed made with fresh linen. Before long, he was joined by the green-headed duck who asked him, 'Are you the Herdsman of Cruachan?'

'I am,' he replied.

'Do you know who were here last night?' asked the duck.

'I do not,' the Herdsman said.

'The big giant, the King of Sorcha, your wife and the shaggy dun filly, and the giant was threatening that if he could get hold of you he would take off your head.'

'I thoroughly believe you,' said the Herdsman.

The duck then gave him food and drink and sent him to bed. She rose next morning, made breakfast for him, and baked a bannock for him to eat on his journey. He set off and walked all day, and again saw a little house in the evening. He went in, and there was the fire, the clean house and the freshly made bed. This time, he was joined by the fox of the scrubwood who asked him if he was the Herdsman of Cruachan.

'I am he,' was the reply.

'Do you know who was here last night?' asked the fox.

'I do not,' said the Herdsman.

'The big giant, King of Sorcha, with your wife and the shaggy dun filly, and the giant was threatening that if he could get hold of you he would take off your head.'

'I do believe it,' said the Herdsman.

The fox then gave him food and drink, and sent him to bed. He rose in the morning, and baked a bannock for the Herdsman

to take on his journey. The Herdsman set off, and in the evening
he saw a house as he had done on the three previous evenings.
Here, too, was the fire burning brightly, the clean house and the
newly made bed. The brown otter of the burn came in, and
asked him the usual question.

'Are you the Herdsman of Cruachan?'

'I am,' was the reply.

'Do you know who were here last night?' asked the brown
otter of the burn.

'I do not,' said the Herdsman.

'The big giant, King of Sorcha, your wife and the shaggy dun
filly, and the giant was threatening that if he had you here he
would take off your head.'

'I certainly believe it,' said the Herdsman of Cruachan.

He was then given food and drink and sent to bed. And when
he wakened in the morning, he saw the hawk of Glencuaich, the
green-headed duck, the fox of the scrubwood and the brown
otter of the burn dancing together on the floor. They all
prepared his breakfast for him, and they ate it together.

'If at any time you are in difficulties,' they told him, 'think
of us and we will help you.'

Then they said goodbye to him and went away.

On the evening of that day, the Herdsman arrived at the cave
where the big giant, King of Sorcha, lived, and there before
him stood his own wife. The giant was away from home,
hunting. The Herdsman kissed his wife, who was delighted
to see him. She gave her husband food, and hid him at the far
end of the cave, covering him with clothes that he might not
be seen.

When the giant came home, he sniffed the air and cried out,
'I! O! Hohagaich! I smell a stranger in this cave.'

'No, my love,' said the Herdsman's wife, 'it is only a little bird that I have roasted that you smell.'

'Oh, if that be it, then I don't care,' said the giant.

She then said to him, 'I wish, my dear, that you would tell where your life is kept, that I may take good care of it.'

'It is in a grey stone over there,' replied the giant.

When he went away next day, she took the grey stone and dressed it, and placed it at the far end of the cave. In the evening, the giant asked, 'What is it that you have dressed there?'

'Your own life,' she replied, 'and we must be careful of it.'

'I see that you are very fond of me'—the giant smiled—'but my life is not there.'

'Where is it then?' she asked.

'It is in a grey sheep on that hillside over there,' he said.

When the giant was away next day, she seized the grey sheep, took it in, dressed it and placed it at the far end of the cave. On his return in the evening, the giant asked, 'What is it that you have dressed there?'

'Your own life, my love,' she said.

'Aha!' he laughed. 'It is not there that it is.'

'Well, I don't know!' exclaimed the woman. 'You have put me to a great deal of trouble taking care of it, and that is twice now you have lied to me about your life.'

'All right,' said the giant, 'now I shall tell you the truth. My life is below the feet of the big horse in the stable. There is a small lake under there. Over the lake are seven grey hides, and over the hides are seven sods of earth, and under all these are seven oak planks. There is a trout in the lake, and a duck in the stomach of the trout, an egg in the stomach of the duck, and a thorn of blackthorn inside the egg—and till that thorn is chewed small I cannot be killed. Whenever the seven grey hides, the seven sods of earth, and the seven oak planks are touched I shall feel it, wherever I may be. I have an axe above the door, and unless all these are cut through with one blow of it, the lake will not be reached, and when it will be reached, I shall feel it.'

When the giant went off hunting next day, the wife told the Herdsman of Cruachan what the King of Sorcha had told her, and she suggested they make an attempt to cut through the hides, sods and planks with the axe.

They went to the stable and, as the Herdsman took down the axe, the big dappled horse suddenly spoke.

'You hold the axe,' it said, 'and I will strike it, for you are not strong enough.'

The Herdsman held the axe on top of the seven grey hides, the seven sods and the seven oak planks, and the big dappled horse rose on his fore-legs and drove the axe through them with a single blow, until it reached the lake. The trout then sprang out of the lake into a river near by, and they could not catch it.

'If I had the brown otter of the burn,' said the Herdsman, 'it would not take long to catch the trout.'

As he spoke, the brown otter of the burn appeared and said, 'What do you wish, Herdsman of Cruachan?'

'I wish that you would get for me the trout that has sprung into the river,' he replied.

The brown otter dived into the river, and he found the trout and gave it to the Herdsman, who opened it. Out sprang a duck and flew into the air, and could not be found.

'If I had the hawk of Glencuaich,' said the Herdsman, 'it would not take long to catch the duck.'

The hawk appeared and asked, 'What do you wish, Herdsman of Cruachan?'

' I wish that you would catch the duck that is flying away there,' he replied.

The hawk soared up after the duck and caught it, and the Herdsman opened the duck, and an egg sprang out of it into the air. He then said, ' If I had the green-headed duck, it would not take long to find the egg for me.'

The duck came as he finished speaking and said to him, ' What do you wish, Herdsman of Cruachan ? '

' Go as fast as you can,' said the Herdsman, ' and get the egg that has sprung into the air. I am sure the big giant is nearly here.'

The green-headed duck went and found the egg, and the Herdsman broke it. The thorn sprang out of it and went into a thorn-bush that was near him, and it was impossible to tell it from any other thorn. The footsteps of the giant could be heard in the distance.

' Ah ! ' sighed the Herdsman, ' if I had the fox of the scrub-wood, he would not take long to find the thorn for me.'

The fox appeared instantly, and said to him, ' What do you wish, Herdsman of Cruachan ? '

' Go as fast as you ever went in your life,' said the Herdsman, ' and find for me the thorn that has sprung out of the egg ; it is in that thorn-bush.'

The fox went swiftly and found the thorn and gave it to the Herdsman, who chewed it. The giant, who was within twenty yards of him, fell down there, cold and dead.

The Herdsman mounted the giant's big dappled horse, and his wife mounted the shaggy dun filly which the giant had stolen from them. And together they rode home to Cruachan. And unless they have died since, then they are alive still.

The Blue Men of the Minch 〜➣

THE Blue Men lived under the sea near the Shiant Isles, and were much feared by the sailors who had to sail their boats through the strait of the Minch. When the Blue Men were awake, they disturbed the waters even on the most peaceful days and dragged down ships to their doom at the bottom of the sea. Their strait was calm only when they were asleep in their underwater caves or when they floated happily on the top of the water. And if they were seen playing and laughing off the headland of Rudha Hunish, then the people of North-western Skye were warned that a wild storm was on its way. The fishermen believed that the Blue Men often followed their boats, and, when the weather grew suddenly rough, they might seize hold of the helm or keel and try to swamp them. The Blue Men particularly disliked to see any large vessel dare to sail in their waters, and some captains were so afraid of these fierce men of the deep sea they would sail northwards round the Shiant Isles rather than take the short cut through the strait.

Some of the Blue Men were always posted at certain spots in the water, and, as soon as they sighted a vessel, they would dive off to tell their Chief, who immediately called together the rest of his followers. Then a great horde of these unfriendly mermen attacked the ship in question. But, first, the Chief shouted a challenge in two lines of Gaelic verse, and only if the skipper could not reply with two lines of verse was the ship seized and wrecked.

173

One day, when the wind was screaming across the sea and whipping the waves into a fury, a great ship, its white sails blowing bravely, appeared at the southern end of the strait. The Blue Men on guard gave the usual warning to their Chief, and soon an army of them arose to the surface of the sea and gazed in wonder at the handsome ship as it swiftly ploughed its way towards them. Some of them grasped the keel but it was too heavy for them to move, others banged the side of the vessel but the smooth planks were too thick for them to pierce.

The Chief pulled himself waist high out of the waves and shouted to the captain.

' What do you want, Chief of the Blue Men ? ' shouted the brave skipper.

The Chief called out his first two lines of verse :

> ' Man of the black cap, what do you say
> As your proud ship cleaves the brine ? '

The Captain promptly replied with his two lines :

> ' My speedy ship takes the shortest way
> And I'll follow you line by line.'

The Chief of the Blue Men sang out :

> ' My men are eager, my men are ready
> To drag you below the waves.'

The Captain sang back :

> ' My ship is speedy, my ship is steady ;
> If it sank it would wreck your cave.'

The Chief had never before been answered so well and so quickly. He knew himself to be outwitted and he and his men sank quickly below the waves, while the ship went peacefully on its way through the Minch.

The Son of the Hen-Wife 🌿

THERE was once a Hen-wife who looked after the poultry of a landlord with a fine great property. This Hen-wife was well off under the landlord : she had a house, three cows and everything else she needed. She also had a handsome young son who went off each day with the cows and kept a careful eye on them. One day he drove the cattle rather farther than usual, to a place where the grass was very green and rich. He was sitting on a hillock while the animals cropped the grass in front of him when a young maiden, with the red of the rose on her cheek and her golden hair hanging down in ringlets over her shoulders, came towards him from the hollow. She greeted him in friendly fashion and asked him if he were not lonely sitting there, herding his three cows.

' I am not lonely now you are with me,' he replied gallantly.

The maiden smiled at him, and then looked towards the cows.

' They are good cattle,' she said. ' Would you sell me one ? '

' Oh, no, indeed, I must not,' said the lad, ' for my mother would scold me.'

' She would not scold you,' replied the maiden, ' if you were given good value for the cow.'

' And what would you give me for her ? ' asked the boy.

' I could give you a charm-stone,' she said.

' And what use would that be ? '

' With it in your hand, you could wish yourself to be in any place you liked, and you would be there in an instant.'

The maiden handed him the stone

The maiden handed him the stone, which was beautiful to look at as it sparkled in the palm of the boy's hand. He decided to test its powers before he exchanged a cow for it. He was thirsty and wished that he might drink from the spring of the Red-stone behind his mother's house. No sooner had the thought come into his mind than he was sitting beside the well. He took a drink and returned in the same way in which he came. Well satisfied, he then gave the cow to the maiden in return for the stone.

He returned home with his two cows at dusk that evening. His mother met him near the byre.

'Where is the third cow, my son?' she demanded to know.

He told her that it had been sold and that he had received a charm-stone in exchange. His mother was very angry with him and scolded him dreadfully. He listened to her calmly until her fury abated.

'Well, go and milk the two cows we have left, you silly boy,' said his mother.

He did so, and that night the two cows gave as much milk as the three had done before.

The next day he drove the cows to the same place he had taken them to the day before, and he sat down again on the same hillock. It was not long before he saw the maiden approaching.

'Will you sell me another cow today?' she asked.

'Indeed, I will not,' he retorted. 'I had a terrible scolding from my mother last night because of the cow I sold you yesterday.'

'Oh, she'll not scold you,' said the maiden, 'if you get good value for her.'

'What, then, will you give me for her?' asked the lad.

'I will give you a healing jewel,' she replied. 'It will heal any disease of your body or mind if you rub it against you.'

The boy had a sore on his toe where he had stubbed it against a stone, so he asked the maiden to lend him the jewel. He rubbed it gently against his toe and, in an instant, the sore was healed. Then he gave her the cow she asked for, and kept the jewel.

He drove home the remaining cow at dusk. His mother met him as he came up the lane towards the house.

'Why is there only one cow, my son?' she demanded to know.

He told her what had happened and, again, she flew into a rage. When she was calmer, she told him to milk the remaining cow. The lad did so, and she gave as much milk as the three cows together had done.

In the morning, the lad drove the cow to the usual spot, and he sat down on the same hillock. The maiden soon came to him and asked him if he would sell her the last cow.

'Indeed, I dare not,' replied the lad. 'I'll never forget the scolding my mother gave me last night.'

'You will not get a scolding,' said the maiden, 'if you get good value for the cow.'

'And what then will you give me for this, our last, cow?' he asked.

'I will give you a little bird-net,' she replied.

'What sort of birds will the net catch and how is it to be set?' asked the lad.

'You have only to spread it on the tops of the bushes,' said the maiden, 'and leave it there all night, and in the morning it will be full of all the kinds of birds you have ever seen or heard, and there will also be in it twelve birds the like of which you have never seen or heard.'

The lad gave the cow for the bird-net without further argument.

When his mother saw that he came home that evening without any cow at all, she could not utter a word. She looked woefully at her son and turned away from him. He was very sorry he had displeased her, but he was sure that she would be satisfied when she saw the number of birds he had caught in his net in the morning.

As soon as he arose next day, he went to see the net which he had set the night before. Never had he seen such a catch of birds! He went home with them and told his mother how he had caught them.

'And will you be able to catch more with this net?' asked his mother.

'I shall get this number every time I set it,' said her son.

The Hen-wife was now better pleased. And it turned out that they had never been so well off with the milk of the cows as they were with the flesh of the birds. And when the lad grew older, he married the landlord's daughter. She was exceedingly beautiful, and people called her Berry-eye.